PALMS

by Desmond Muirhead

Dale Stuart King, Publisher

Six Shooter Canyon, Globe, Arizona

Copyright 1961 by Dale Stuart King

Lithographed in the U. S. A.

by Ampco, Phoenix, Arizona

Library of Congress Catalog Card No. 60-16856
Cover: *Washingtonia robusta*

Contents

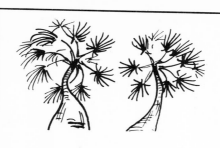

Pritchardia beccariana

INTRODUCTION

Of all the powerful plant forms which grace the landscape of the warmer countries, there is nothing to rival the palms. Wherever you see them they are the centers of attention. The other artifacts of both man and nature are but poor competition.

There has been a great revival of interest in these trees in America recently, and many more palms are being planted in the Southwest, on the Gulf Coast and in Florida than ever before. Usually they are arranged haphazardly in gardens, parks, or cities with little thought of their ultimate effect. This book has been written to fill a gap in the recognition and knowledge of the different types of palms, and to guide people to plant them to improve the landscape, rather than to mar it.

Although it is specifically directed to people living in Arizona and California, those living in Florida, Hawaii, and other warm or sub-tropical areas should find it useful, as practically all the palms mentioned will grow wherever they are hardy. In addition a special selection has been made of some of the best tropical palms for use in landscape design.

Because of the format of the book it has been impossible to avoid a certain amount of duplication. However the layout is specifically organized to make information easily available and perhaps this will make up for any such repetition.

During the writing of this book, I have received many helpful suggestions from numerous people. Mr. David Barry, Jr., of Los Angeles, California and Mr. William Hertrich of the Huntington Botanic Garden, San Marino, have been generous with their time and information, as have Messrs. Will Beittel of Santa Barbara; F. A. Tetley III of Corona; Walter Andersen of San Diego; Otto Martens of Arcadia; Richard Schnabel of Palm Springs; and Leonard Etter of Phoenix.

Help by mail was rendered by Mrs. Lucita Waite of Miami, Florida. She is the charming secretary of the Palm Society. Anyone who is at all interested in these plants should be a member of this excellent organization. Mrs. Waite's address is 7229 S. W. 54th Avenue, Miami 43, Florida (U.S.A.) A letter or card to her will elicit an immediate response accompanied by a rising flood of literature on palms and other suitable propaganda for the society.

More help by mail came from Dr. Walter Hodge, Longwood Gardens, Pennsylvania; Bud Hallberg of Arcadia; John Spring of San Francisco; Ernest Fisher of Portland; Brian Mulligan of Seattle; Herbert Warren of Victoria, B. C., Canada. Also from D. H. Ransom of the Island of Jersey; Mr. Jayaweera of Kandy, Ceylon; Commander Dorrien Smith of the Scilly Isles; and Mr. Campbell, curator of the Royal Botanic Garden, Kew, England.

Thanks are also due Graham Warrington whose great photographs were specifically taken for and comprise the bulk of those in the book; Josef Muench who allowed me to look through his excellent files; Karl Obert, Samuel Gottscho, and Nixon Smiley who sent fine selections for me to choose from.

I must also thank my Phoenix office for their help, especially towards the end when my zeal was waning and my enthusiasm flagging. John Averill, my Phoenix partner, Timothy Cochrane, Joan Sprague, and Frances Grant were invaluable.

Finally I must thank my wife for so pleasantly putting up with the littered rooms and shattered schedules of the part-time author in full-time orbit, who in the immortal words of H. B. Dunnington-Grubb "fell by accident and without qualification into society's worst-paid profession."

1

PALMS

The Palms are members of the family Palmaceae, comprising more than 4,000 different species. They vary from ground-hugging dwarfs like the *Serenoas* of Florida to the Giant Wax Palms of the Andes in South America, which may reach 200 feet. There are straight palms like dates, curving palms like coconuts, and even climbing palms, like the rattans of Malaya, from which the familiar rattan furniture is made. These may wind their way for several hundred feet before they reach the sunlight. This makes it very difficult to get at their flowers to classify them: a characteristic which is true, unfortunately, of most palms and which has delayed study on them in the past.

As well as being ornamental, palms serve a multitude of uses, supporting whole populations by their bounty. The classic example is the coconut, which provides food, drink, shelter, and clothing to the grateful people who live in its shade. Other palms are sources for wax, medicine, raffia, oil, fat, thread, fibres, fans, baskets, and so on. Demand exceeds supply for coconut oil, from which oleomargerine is made. Palmolive soap is another familiar product made from palm oil.

The vast majority of palms are straight-trunked, with a crown of fan or feather-shaped leaves at the top. They are monocotyledonous plants, related to grasses, bamboos, lilies and the like, and are unique in this class of plants because of their height and of their trunk development. These trunks are quite different from trees like elms or beeches: they have no true cambium layer and do not add rings of growth annually. In fact, the trunks of some palms even shrink with age. In addition, the palm trunk is soft inside, with scattered conducting vessels, each surrounded by an incredibly tough outer ring of hard fibres. This hollow cylinder type of construction enables them to resist high winds, even hurricanes.

Many palm trunks are most ornamental. Some are narrow-ringed and glossy like bamboos. Others are huge, massive, and dominating like forest-grown trees. Leaves may be small, from little bigger than the palm of a human hand to enormous fans which may be 20 or more feet across — or feathers which have been known to reach 60 feet in length and 8 feet in width or thickness.

The flowers of palms vary considerably, too, from small, invisible clusters borne amongst the leaves, to the 20-foot-long structure of the Indian Talipot which, almost unique among the palms, precedes its death. The fruits are every colour of the rainbow and are an exceptionally spectacular scarlet in certain types, such as *Arcontophoenix*, *Veitchia*, and *Actinophloeus*. All these palms command the scene when they are in fruit. The palm family also includes the double coconut which bears the largest seed known to man, weighing perhaps 50 pounds and taking up to 10 years to mature.

HARDINESS OF PALMS

The hardiness of plants is a very difficult thing to assess and depends on so many variable characteristics. Going through Palm Springs recently, I noticed most bougainvilleas in certain parts of the town had been killed to the ground, but for some reason certain isolated specimens which were fully exposed had been left untouched and were still blooming freely. I found out later that gardens within two

The Windmill palm (Trachycarpus) *shown on the shores of Lake Maggiore Italy; opposite is the beautiful island of Isola Bella. This palm has often withstood temperatures of 0° F.*

blocks of each other experienced minimum temperatures varying 10° F.

Even the home garden has several different climatic zones in it. That under the patio roof may be ten degrees warmer than another area in the open. A handkerchief supported by pencils over the lawn will stop the earth heat radiating outwards on a clear night. The area underneath is 8 degrees or more warmer than an adjacent unprotected area. Tree canopies act in the same way.

South and southwest corners may trap the sun on a warm winter's day and will affect considerably the temperatures of the following night. Here one must beware of too much sun on a tender palm that has just endured

a cold night. Incidentally, it is often the several months of these cold nights in California which are the limiting factors to the growth of sub-tropical palms, rather than the low freezing temperatures. Therefore the 10 degrees of difference on normal nights counts as much as the occasional really low temperature.

When choosing a site for a warm microclimate, areas near large bodies of water should be considered, if possible, since they are usually more temperate than areas inland. Hill slopes with good drainage are warmer than low-lying frost pockets. This is because the cold air is heavier and rolls downhill at night, collecting in the valleys and forcing the warm air up

3

to the hill slopes. This may make a difference of 5-10 degrees in the minimum temperature.

There are no really frost-free areas in California. The imaginary line denoting freedom from frost starts halfway between Guaymas, Mexico, and the U. S. border 200 miles away. Coconuts, though small and stunted, can be grown in Guaymas. They are still dwarfed at LaPaz, but they get progressively better looking as you travel down the coast to Acapulco. In California the apparent hardiness of plants is set back by cyclical bad frosts occurring every 10 years or so when the thermometer usually hits 25° or 26° F. on the coast. This temperature may recur perhaps for three successive nights.

At the same time, as far inland as Pasadena, it might hit 20°-22° F., and 18° F. or slightly less at Riverside, Palm Springs, Indio, or Phoenix. Hillslopes in the same areas might be 5-7 degrees warmer. These frosts have occurred so far with an alarming regularity in 1913, 1922, 1937, and 1949. We are due for another one any time. For this reason, most of the palms listed in the temperate section of this book are hardy to 20° F. or better. Some palms are even hardier than this, especially when they are older. Canary Island dates and Butias have all withstood low temperatures of between 10° F. and 15° F. in not-too-isolated incidences. The Windmill Palm (see page 32) is being grown in the open in Edinburgh, Scotland, in Victoria, Canada, in Portland, Oregon, and in Hampton, Virginia. This palm is obviously hardy in the more protected sites of many places where it is not at present known.

For the enthusiast who likes growing plants which are marginal for their region, there are a few spots in California which are very close to being frost free. On hill slopes, in the banana belts above La Jolla or Golita, there may be areas that are not hit in the average cyclical frost, but sooner or later one worse than the others is likely to get them.

One need not become alarmed about these freezes, since all of the attractive tender varieties listed here will stand 2 or 3 degrees of frost, and, if they are good, established trees, they may be damaged at 26° F., but will probably come through. In fact, the whole coastal region between Santa Barbara and San Diego can grow *Howeas* and *Arcontophoenix* outside in protected locations. With more care the avid enthusiast could grow many other borderline palms for at least 20 years in inland areas; but this, obviously, cannot be a recommended practice for landscape architects and others interested primarily in design.

To give an example, there are some fine *Howeas* under a live oak at the Huntington Botanic Garden which, with the aid of citrus oil stoves during the bad freeze of 1949, have been growing since the early 1940's, although there have been numerous minor freezes to contend with since, as well as the three days in 1949 when the thermometer hit 20° F. for three nights running, as it had done in 1937, 1922, and in 1913. There are other tender palms as well, such as *Arcontophoenix* or Seaforthias which are widely grown in the Pasadena, San Marino area.

With similar occasional care these palms could be grown as far north as San Francisco, especially in a lath-covered patio. In northern regions like this, lightish, well-drained soil is important since it will warm quickly in the sun. Damp, heavy soils are cold, due to the reluctance of water to change temperature, owing to its low specific heat.

The worst types of freezes are those which occur early in the season when the sap is still up the tree in fall or early winter. This is where an interior court, a warm glass window and a tree to ward off the morning sun will really help; for although these freezes are not common in the Southwest, only a very few degrees can do severe damage.

Summer temperatures are also limiting factors to palm growth. Many palms will burn at 120° F., but they will probably recover. Those that do are noted in the section on individual trees. However, a sensible attitude toward desert gardening in the Southwest would provide automatic atomizers or fogsprayers for the patio in summer and radiant floor heat in winter. This is necessary for human comfort and it would provide an almost perfect home for half-hardy palms as well, either in the gound or in pots.

There is also a question of appropriateness. Although an occasional palm is interesting in the coastal belt from San Francisco to Carmel, there are so many other beautiful trees and shrubs which are more at home there that one cannot help feeling palms should not be emphasized in this particular area—when they grow so much better elsewhere.

FINDING TEMPERATURE RANGE IN YOUR AREA.

If you ring up your local weather station, usually located at the airport, the chief climatologist will tell you the average and minimum temperatures for your area. You can also check these with a minimum thermometer.

You may have to adjust the results if you are on a hillslope or in a valley. For instance, the thermometer hit 18° F. in Old Town, San Diego, in 1937, while it only registered 30° F. on some of the surrounding hillsides. This when all the books say that San Diego is frost-free! For those regions with inadequate local data, Sunset's Western Garden book has some good notes on climatic zones for the western states.

SOIL PREPARATION AND FERTILIZATION

(For pots and indoor planting see page 48.)

There is a very old adage which says spend one dollar on the tree, ten dollars on the hole. This may be an exaggeration, but it is safe to say that no other group of trees responds more readily to a large hole and plenty of manure, fertilizer and water.

Most palms will grow in practically any well-drained soil. (Sabals and Paurotis will thrive in standing water, but they are exceptional.) Queen palms will grow in *caliche* (limy, clay hardpan) holes in San Diego, but even a casual glance at the streets of that city will show that they do not like it. In areas where caliche is widespread, like Tucson, we specify a 5 by 5 by 5 feet hole with 15 pounds of sulphur to lower the pH or alkalinity and ⅔ yard of cow manure for food. The hole is filled with the best and richest topsoil available. Drainage is essential and must under such conditions be provided either by drilling through the bottom of the hole to a gravelly area below, or by linking a series of planting holes to a rock pit. Alternatively you could build new soil up above the caliche and surround it with a planting box.

5

If you are at any time in doubt about the need for rich soil, try two palms planted together, one with a huge hole filled with a ton of manure and black soil, another with little soil preparation. Dent Smith did this with two African oil palms, writes Douglas Knapp in *Principes*. The latter plant made poor growth but the former one "grew mightily, and when only 6 years old had leaves 18 feet long — longer than any I have seen on a plant of its age."

Wherever you are, dig as big a hole as time and your back will stand. Even if you have naturally good soil it will pay you to prepare it well, since nothing looks worse than a ratty palm which is just managing to survive.

If you do dig a big hole, half fill it with compost, kitchen refuse, clay, cow or stable manure and grass clippings, and place masses of good rich topsoil above this. If you have a chance, dig the hole several months before you plant to let the earth settle and to allow decay to start.

The best time to move palms is in the spring and summer months when the nights are warm and new roots are being put out. They can be planted successfully in the winter however; at which time special care

must be taken not to break the root ball, or the palm will have a miserable, tired appearance for as much as an entire season, before it finally recovers.

If the seedlings are planted from the nursery row, or if the plants are from containers smaller in size than a 5 gallon can, they will be aided by some shade for the first year or two. Palms moved and transplanted directly from a lath house will often die from sun or frost if they are not protected during this first season.

The palm is set in the hole and a depression must be established around it and hilled up at the edge to take the irrigation water. New palms should be flooded for several hours at least once a week. Great care must be taken to see that the irrigation water can seep down to drainage so that the palm is not exposed to a soggy soil.

After the palm is safely in the ground, the water supply is the most limiting factor to successful palm growth. I will again quote Dent Smith, the founder of the Palm Society. "It is virtually impossible to over-irrigate a palm that has perfect drainage," he says.

A 6-inch mulch or layer of manure, compost, or peat, all in as advanced a state of decay as possible will complete the planting. This should be dug in every spring and repeated. Most palms also relish commercial fertilizer, two further applications of which are recommended each year. Organic fertilizers are preferred, but chemicals are also widely used. Large established palms will take 10 to 15 pounds of fertilizer at a time. This may be spread in the irrigation circle or plugged into the lawn by 18-inch deep holes, made with a crowbar in con-

Palms have appeared in the art and literature of many nations.

centric circles around the tree, in an area equivalent to the extent of the roots. Small palms will take 1 to 5 pounds of a balanced fertilizer, depending on their size and vigor. Many palms with yellow foliage would still have fine green leaves if they were fed occasionally. A nutritional spray applied through the fronds will often have an electric effect on palms with poor foliage. The last application of fertilizer, if high in phosphorus and potassium, is reputed to help harden the palm before cold fall weather sets in.

When palms are planted in lawns, a 6 foot ring of bare earth around the newly-planted tree is recommended for at least 2 years. This should be cultivated with a hoe as often as possible to keep the soil aerated. The leaves are usually tied up vertically until strong new growth is being made. This is to protect the bud or growing point. Palms have only one of these, and if it is lost the tree dies.

If all this seems like a lot of trouble it should be pointed out that palms are really rough and tough and will often get by and even ultimately make fine specimens if they are just stuck in the ground and left to their own devices, as long as they are watered.

It is also surprising how quickly they will grow to a size where they will have some effect in the landscape if a little care is given them; and how magnificent they will look if care is lavished on them.

MOVING LARGE PALMS

This has become a specialist performance in the West in recent years and for as little as $25 (a small date palm) or as much as $10,000 (a large *Chamaerops humilis*) a mature palm

RAY MANLEY

Moving a 15-ton Washingtonia filifera *palm at the Del Webb Hiway House, Tucson, Arizona.*

can be planted in your garden. As an average, a good-looking tree of many different species can usually be obtained for between $5 and $15 per trunk foot.

Palms move more easily as large trees than any other comparable groups and if the required precautions are religiously followed, there will be remarkably few losses. Although an experienced operator can move large palms at any time in the year, *the warm spring and summer months from April to September are the best*. In fact the hotter the better, and the most successful transplants are made in July and August when root growth is at a maximum. Unlike dicotyledonous trees which often make comparatively vigorous root growth in mild winter climates, palms make hardly any roots at all over the winter. They also have an unusual method of forming new roots. *These are made from the crown where the bottom of the trunk comes first in contact with the soil.* This is the reason why palms, even those with no visible roots at all, move so easily. In fact, those roots which have been cut during the original digging are practically useless after this, so that new roots must be made immediately to sustain the tree. Hence the importance of planting at the season of maximum root growth.

Obviously if you cut a trench around the palm a year or even a month before you move it and fill this trench with good topsoil, when you do come to move the palm you will get as much as a complete set of new roots. When this cannot be done, take as large a ball as you can get, both to retain as many of the original feeding roots as possible, and to give the tree stability in wind and weather by lowering its

center of gravity. We specify 4-foot root balls on all large palms, since our interest is more than a successful transplant. We want the tree to recover and to look vigorous and healthy as soon as possible.

Like other types of trees, palms recently moved should have their foliage reduced to balance the reduction in the roots. The number of leaves varies with the type of palm and is a matter of trial and error for each district, in most instances. Certainly no trials and tests have been made on this or any other function of palm care in spite of the fact that in the Southwest alone moving palms is a business involving at least $20 million annually. As with smaller plants the leaves are also tied up firmly around the growing point to protect it for the first few months. The root balls should be protected in transit preferably by a covering of wet burlap.

The palms are usually moved in with a boom truck or drag line and are supported by wires and chains. A small tractor with a front-end-loader is usually employed to get the palm into exactly the right position. Accidentally banging the trunk around or letting it fall on the ground may be fatal, so be careful. After it has been lowered into the hole it is set a little deeper than its original position to encourage the new root growth at the crown, then good soil is shovelled in around the roots, and the loader is banged on the ground to compact the soil and to get a firm union with the tree. This must be properly done, for otherwise new roots are reluctant to leave the root ball. The tree is then "watered in" to remove all air pockets.

During the first season, as with small palms, watering is the most important requirement of the newly-planted trees. The hose should be allowed to run in the irrigation depression about 8 hours twice a week at least for the first 2 months. Subsequently most palms should have an all day or all night soaking once a week. You will soon find by this method whether or not the drainage is adequate. You will also find that if your water is highly alkaline the leaves of some palms may go yellow. An application of manganese sulfate or chelated iron will usually correct this, if it is not caused by cold or by nitrogen deficiency.

When purchasing large palms, remember to take note of the trunk condition. A tree which has been neglected for several seasons will not produce an increase in its existing trunk girth when good cultural practices are resumed. A fatter trunk above a mean skinny one is not very handsome and occasionally a palm will show starvation waists for alternate periods of neglect and care.

A last word of warning: if you do move large palms in the winter months, try to acquire specimens already growing in your locality. Very heavy losses may be expected from palms transported over long distances at this time of the year. I am particularly referring to palms brought into Arizona and California from Texas, but the shock of a new climate, plus lack of root growth is often too much for palms wherever they are planted.

PRUNING PALMS

Some palms like *Arcontophoenix* species and the Guadalupe palms are self-pruning, but many others retain their leaves for varying lengths of time, usually long enough to look unsightly, like the Senegal dates and Queen palms or, occasionally, indefinitely like the *Washingtonias*. As a general rule remove all untidy, dead,

yellow, brown or otherwise unattractive foliage as soon as it appears. *Washingtonias* can be pruned in early spring just before they make their new fronds, but don't give them a "French haircut." Leave some fronds below the horizontal or the tree will not look right for months again. Frozen leaves may also be removed, but wait at least one season before removing apparently frozen trees. Palms have remarkable powers of recovery and many trees which at one time appeared completely dead have recovered and have lived to a ripe old age.

The act of pruning is accomplished in many different ways. An ordinary saw or a pruning saw will solve most problems. For the old leaf bases, not the leaves, on *Washingtonia robusta* or *Chamaerops humilis,* a linoleum knife is best. On the *robusta* a man climbs up the tree with climbing irons and with a rope round his middle. As he climbs he slashes horizontally at the grey leaf bases, leaving a series of

Well-trimmed date trunk.

9

attractive notched scars which are at first a rich mahogany brown in color but which are later destined to turn grey. *Robustas* will keep a much better color in the desert regions, and the drier coastal regions such as San Diego, than they will in the damper climates.

Dates and similar trees with peg-like projections can be pruned to a beautiful trunk pattern (see photograph) if the leaf stubs are cut evenly to the same length, at the end of each season. If they are already unevenly pruned they can be given a diamond trim, which removes the projections altogether. Some trees like *Erythea brandigeei* and *Butia capitata* have trunks which normally do not look comfortable with their leaf projections left on. They should either be used as background trees or cut clean to a smooth trunk. For trees with excessively thick leaf stalks like Canary Island Dates, or for those with a heavy shag like *Washingtonia filifera,* power saws or axes are used.

Obviously most palms need a certain amount of pruning maintenance. In my opinion, they are so interesting they are worth it, but don't plant them if you are not prepared to look after them. If you do, you may be doing yourself or your neighborhood a disservice.

PROPAGATION

All palms are propagated by seeds or division. Palms, like dates, which have definite horticultural varieties such as the Deglet Noor, the Zahidi or the Medjool, are increased vegetatively by offshoots removed from the base of the parent tree. *Chamaerops humilis, Raphis sp., Phoenix reclinata, Caryotas, Chamaedoreas, Chrysalidocarpus* and other clump or cluster palms can be divided. If the offshoots or suckers are well rooted, they can be detached from the parent plant with as much earth as possible and planted out in good soil, preferably during the spring or summer months. For success this must be done with great care, as it is a delicate operation. At least half the foliage should be removed when the palm is in its new location.

If these offshoots are not rooted, suitable underground stems may be sliced half through with a sharp knife. This will cut off some of the food and water and will force the stem to make roots above the cut to support itself. After it is well rooted in a month or two, the new plant may be severed from the parent and can be potted or planted as desired.

Most palms germinate readily from seed. If you have difficulty in finding a local source for them, seeds of over a hundred different species may be obtained from the Palm Society, c/o Mrs. Lucita Waite, 7229 South West 54th Avenue, Miami 43, Florida.

Fresh seeds are preferable. They may be sown in shallow flats or boxes with drainage holes in their bottoms. The seedlings should be covered to a depth equivalent to the thickness of the seed. During the winter months in subtropical climates they will stand full sun, but they will need lath or slat protection at least during the summer. The seeds should be kept moist but never wet and soggy. On the Pacific Coast or in the desert seeds are best started in the spring, or under glass with bottom heat in the seasons with cold nights. The seedlings will normally sprout in 3 to 10 weeks, although a very few species may take a year or more. As the second leaf begins to grow they should be moved into 3-inch pots or small cans with rocks in the bottom, and a soil mix rich in leaf mould or rotted sod should be used. Species which put down long roots will need larger pots initially.

When the palms are 6 inches to a foot in height they can be transferred to shaded rows in the garden or nursery. Quickly-germinating species such as *Phoenix* or *Washingtonias* can be sown outside in the garden like radishes, if desired, and thinned out as the seedlings sprout.

As the small palms grow, they can be gradually acclimated to heat by exposing them to full sunshine for a few hours a day. Eventually all but the shade-loving species can be moved into full sun, or canned up in 5 gallon cans.

Coconuts are among the most easily grown palms even in temperate climates; they are laid on their sides almost covered with soil and will germinate in 3 to 6 months.

DISEASES OF PALMS

To predators palms are among the most resistant plants known. The only serious pest on the Pacific Coast is the fungus *Penicillium vermoeseni*. This is a fungus thought to cause bud rot, leaf-baserot and trunk canker on a number of different species. *Washingtonia filifera* is particularly susceptible, and since the fungus thrives in cool damp weather, this species is no longer recommended for coastal planting. However, the disease is certainly not common in the desert on this species. *Phoenix canariensis, Arecastrum romanzoffianum* and *Arcontophoenix cunninghamiana* are less often affected and can be saved by a Capstan spray if the disease has not gone too far. Palms which are beyond repair should be burned to prevent the fungus spreading.

HOW TO RECOGNIZE THE PALMS AND WHERE TO FIND THEM

Most palms tend to look alike until you know them. Of course they are actually differentiated by botanical characteristics, notably by their flowers and fruits. However you do not need to be a botanist to become familiar with the more common varieties of palms. Much in the same way that during the war cadets found it possible to recognize an airplane picture flashed on the screen for seconds, you can identify most palms from their general aspects. The drawings in this book have been purposely done to illustrate the landscape character of each tree, and to facilitate the easy recognition of the different species.

Apart from the initial division of palms into those with fan-shaped foliage and those with feather-like foliage (see photographs) there are many variations of size, color, and conformation of trunk, leaf and fruit. Some are very easily recognized by their leaf color, like the Mexican blue palm and the Butia palm; others by the persistence of their old leaves like the *Washingtonias;* still others by their great size, like the Canary Island dates, or the Chilean wine palms. Some have black hairy trunks like the Windmill palm, some spiny brown trunks like *Trithrinax. Arcontophoenix* and many tropical palms such as *Veitchia, Dictyosperma* and *Roystonea* have a green super-column of sheathing leaf bases which connects the trunk to the crown. *Chamaerops humilis* and *Phoenix reclinata* are naturally clump forming, as are the bamboo palms, the *Raphis,* and many of the *Chamaedorea* species.

GRAHAM WARRINGTON

Feather leaves, date

12

The minimum temperature requirements will also help narrow the range so that you will know you are not confronted by *Pritchardia pacifica* in El Paso, Texas, but you might be in the Florida Keys or in Honolulu. *Howeas,* for instance, are not common in the desert regions except indoors. If you see a fan palm in Las Vegas it is likely to be a *Washingtonia.*

As an aid to recognition you should go and see the extensive collections of palms such as those at the Huntington Botanic Garden in Pasadena, at the Court House grounds in Santa Barbara and at Balboa Park, San Diego. Here, at the Natural History Museum, you can buy a book for 50 cents telling you where to look for the well known palms of the San Diego area. There is also a good collection at the home of J. Harrison Wright in Riverside and another near the clubhouse at Encanto Park Golf Course in Phoenix. In San Francisco, Golden Gate Park has several species, although they rightly have not stressed the palms there.

In Florida the Fairchild Tropical Garden at Coconut Grove should not be missed nor should the Foster Gardens on Nuuanu Avenue in Honolulu. If you happen to be abroad there is a fine collection in the green houses at Kew Gardens, London, and at the famous Botanic Gardens of Singapore and Buitenzorg, Java. However, I doubt whether many people will be

And fans, robustas

GRAHAM WARRINGTON

calling at these latter establishments next week. Rio, Brazil, and Soledad, Cuba, also have good palm collections in their botanic gardens.

Once you have mastered the common varieties of palms, any trip to the warmer areas of the world is likely to be twice as interesting as before; perhaps it will stimulate you to a study of the entire fraternity of trees, for surely they are the world's most sterling and dignified citizens, helping to cover up, as they do, the vast trail of ugliness which machine-age man has everywhere left in his wake.

NOMENCLATURE

The scientific names follow Bailey's *Hortus Second,* although much botanical and horticultural work is needed on the palms, which have received little study in the past. The common names follow, where possible, the suggestions of *Standardized* *Plant Names.* The idea of a standard for common names is good. Unfortunately, this book is a monument of autocratic decision by a few thoughtful men who in actuality had little or no sense of euphony in name production. It is hard to countenance sane people producing a name for popular acceptance like "Mexican Washington palm" or "Springwood white spring heath." As Clarence Elliott suggested, perhaps *Buddleja globosa* should be called "Globose buddle-bush" and *Quercus ambigua,* "Ambiguous quirk."

Where I have felt S.P.N. erred, I have chosen what I considered to be the most suitable of the common names on the Pacific Coast. An arbitrary decision perhaps, but neither the trade nor the profession has accepted S.P.N. on palms anyway. Perhaps this will encourage the publishers to take a second look at what could be a most useful work.

Washingtonia filifera *palm near Palm Springs, California.*

THE HARDY PALM SPECIES

These palms are all hardy to 20° F. or less and can be grown with few exceptions from north of San Francisco to the Mexican border, on the Pacific Coast. Most of them will also thrive in the Arizona and California deserts, although extreme heat becomes the limiting factor under these conditions; this is fully discussed under the separate species. Some of them will grow in New Mexico and southern Texas and all of them will do well on the Gulf Coast east to Florida.

In southern Florida a much wider range of palms may be considered since this is the only sub-tropical climate in the United States. Some of the best for landscape use are discussed on pages 78-93. These palms are also suitable for Hawaii, where few of the hardy palms are needed.

The small group called less-hardy palms can be grown outside from Santa Barbara south on the Pacific Coast as long as they are within reach of the ocean influence. In sheltered locations they are suitable for patios or under roofs or trees as far inland as Phoenix and some of them are common in the San Marino, Pasadena area. This group is also suitable for Florida and Hawaii.

15

THE HARDY FAN PALMS

CHAMAEROPS HUMILIS   *Mediterranean Fan Palm*

Chamaerops in Greek means dwarf.

This unusual tree, the only palm native to Europe, grows wild in Spain and Italy and on the Mediterranean islands of Sardinia and Sicily. Great thickets are also found on the coasts of Algeria and Morocco, in north Africa. Natural stands were once common on the French Riviera, where it was considered one of the last relics of a former ancient, tropical flora. To the landscape architect *Chamaerops* is a fascinating piece of plant sculpture.

The normal habit is shown in the photograph and drawing; several curved trunks, rising from a common base, each support a hemispherical head of foliage. A mature plant may reach 15 or 18 feet but between 6 and 12 is more likely. The trunks—as much as a foot through and dark brown in color — have a handsome, shaggy appearance, due to the persistent leaf bases; these may be cut smooth, if required, with a linoleum knife.

The leaves are stiff, green and usually deeply cut, but these factors as well as their size and general appearance are subject to considerable variation. Some plants even have their leaflets joined like *Livistonas* to form a circular leaf of great interest. The slender spiny leaf stalk may also vary from a few inches to several feet in length; in either case it subtends the leaf with an unusual, parasol-like elegance.

Nursery catalogues list as many as six different forms of *Chamaerops* from low, squat shrubs, *C. humilis nana*, to tall clumps, as wide as they are high. There are also single-stemmed trees. *C. humilis argentea* is a delightful silver-leafed version which provides a relief from the recurring green of dwarf palm plantations.

Normally dioecious, female trees bear conspicuous clusters of reddish-brown fruits. As a rule they must be pollenated by hand, a process easily accomplished by brushing a male panicle over the yellow female flowers. According to Naudin, the late French authority, about 1 plant in 30 is self-fertilizing.

The Mediterranean Fan Palm ranks with the Windmill and Canary Island Date as among the hardiest palms around. Grown in southern England, and occurring, in the past at least, as far north as Scotland, the Mediterranean fan palm will stand an occasional frost, down to 15 or 12 degrees, but repeated cold of this severity will kill it. Although this plant will endure poor soil, drought, wind, heat, cold, and neglect, it responds magnificently to deep rich loam in a sunny location, sheltered by a wall, a building, or a foliage mass. I have seen specimens in Salinas, California, where the lower stems and leaves were protected by a fence and were luxuriant green sprays, but two or three heads above the fence were withered wraiths, ravaged by the fury of the sea winds in that area.

Given good conditions *Chamaerops* palms make fine specimens on the Pacific coast from north of San Francisco (where they do well if protected from wind) to the Mexican border. In addition, they will stand full desert sun—although they perhaps look better with partial shade. There are marvelous specimens in Phoenix, where they like good soil and plenty of water. In Palm Springs the sandy soil must be heavily treated with peat, the trunks should be wrapped in burlap for the first few years and they should be hosed down every two or three days in hot summer weather. Plants of *Chamaerops* may be found throughout Florida, the Gulf Coast, and, of course, Hawaii.

Propagation is usually by seed and germination is fast and easy. When they are 1 year old they may be planted in nursery rows in open ground. Varieties are usually raised

Chamaerops humilis *will grow either as a fine clump or as a single-stemmed tree.*

Chamaerops humilis dominates the entire scene at the Stuart Company's office, Pasadena, California. T. Church was the landscape architect. E. Stone, the architect.

CHAMAEROPS HUMILIS (continued)

from suckers carefully removed in the fall and planted in a moist (not wet), shady place until they have shown vigorous new fronds.

The chief disadvantage of the Mediterranean fan palm is its comparatively slow growth of 6 inches or less a year. Old plants are, consequently, worth a lot of money. Mature palms with several stems may fetch between $2,000 and $10,000, so even at an initial price of $5 to $50 they are an excellent investment. A mulch of stable manure or commercial fertilizer applied annually will eventually give good dividends.

As a landscape subject the Mediterranean fan palm is unsurpassed, with its fine form and character and a presence which demands attention, like the natural aristocrat it is. Even large plants move easily. In all sizes it is useful as a specimen in lawns, planting boxes and tubs, and also in cool greenhouses and indoors. This palm is especially effective with interesting backgrounds like grilles (see photograph), plain walls or murals, and foregrounds of yuccas, aloes or large blue agaves, and in fact all types of succulents and cacti. A background of taller light foliage trees such as *Lysoloma, Jacaranda* or *Albizzia julibrissin* will help set off the tree; so will groups of larger light green palms like *Erythea edulis.*

Named for the Greek Erythea, one of the Hesperides, the daughter of Evening (or the West), who lived on an enchanted island.

The Mexican Blue Palm is native to the dry desert regions of Lower California (Mexico), where it forms dense stands. It can also be seen growing wild across the border from Palm Springs near the town of Calexico. It is a noble, straight-trunked tree growing slowly to 25, occasionally to 40 feet, and bearing a wide head of sharp, ice-blue fan-shaped foliage of an almost breath-taking color and beauty. The leaf stalk is stiff, about 3 feet long, and is armed with hooked spines. The leaf segments number 30 to 50 and are divided to the middle. They point characteristically forward, diverging only slightly from the natural axis of the blade. The spadix on which the grey white flowers and chestnut fruits is borne is also unusual, since it may reach almost to the ground.

In some areas the Mexican blue is subject to tip burn from over-watering with high alkali water. In others, older leaves turn yellow and must be quickly removed, as they are unsightly. There is a great deal of variation in the color of different plants, from a rather unpleasant greeny-blue to an almost ghost-like bright silver. It is to be hoped that some enterprising nurseryman will make selections from the better forms available. The leaves are persistent and a shag, or skirt, which is not attractive in cultivated areas, will form around the trunk and should be religiously cut. Old leaf bases are also persistent on young trees, but the trunks soon look smooth if they are cut off. Mature trees shed these leaf bases, leaving a fine grey trunk marked laterally like a *Jubaea*.

The Mexican Blue Palm is easily grown from seed, sown in spring, especially in a hot bed or greenhouse. The small plants are slow to reach any size, putting on perhaps 6 inches per year. In all sizes they are difficult to move, often taking a season to recover. Some nurserymen and contractors seal the end of their weeping roots with blow torches, or wrap them in paper to reduce the loss of sap.

Mexican blues are very hardy and do well in the drier coastal, interior valley and desert areas of the Southwest, from San Francisco south. They have been known to endure 15° F. temperatures without harm. They normally require full sun, although, in all but the hottest regions, they will survive and thrive without watering after the first season or two, if necessary. They actually like hot, dry conditions, and, therefore, make good pot and tub plants. They also prefer a light, well-drained soil. Like most other palms outside the tropics, they do not grow well in wet soils of any description. In the desert regions they will stand some shade.

Since the Mexican blue is pretty as a small plant, it makes an excellent landscape subject, which tends to eliminate its slow growth as a drawback to planting. Groups of three around an entrance doorway are very striking; so are larger groups backed by dark green foliage such as magnolias, holly, or Carolina cherry laurel. They also make fine focal groups among masses of greener palms against plain white walls, or in patios or courtyards, where a clump of two or three palms of different sizes has an electric effect. When small they are improved by a dark green background of *Carissa*, pittosporum or *Cyperus alternifolia*. Although single specimens of Mexican blues are quite stiff and formal, I do not like to see them in lines or avenues, since one cannot rely on an even development.

Erythea armata, *Mexican Blue Palm*

The second member of the triumvirate is also native to Lower California, near San Jose, Mexico; and is named for T. S. Brandegee, a celebrated botanist, who was once honorary curator of the University of California Herbarium at Berkeley.

The San Jose palm is taller, more slender and less inclined to be straight upright than the other two *Erytheas*. It may reach 50 feet in the Southwest and is credited by some with 100 feet in its native habitat—although Bailey, in *Gentes Herbarum* doubts this. The trunk is smooth and handsome if trimmed, but is quite ugly if the old leaf bases, which are naturally persistent, are allowed to remain on the tree. The leaves are a bright yellow-green and give an impression of refinement and delicacy—especially with the sun shining through them. The old leaves persist as an unattractive petticoat, or skirt, and should be removed every year or two. The blade is divided to the middle, with narrow leaflets. The leafstalks are slender, armed with spines, and about the same length as the blade. The flower stalk is reduced to a normal length rather less than that of the leaves and the fruits are freely borne.

Erythea brandegeei could be a valuable addition to the scene as another alternate to *Washingtonia robusta*, covering the same range of uses. William Hertrich of the Huntington Botanic Garden considers it the finest fan palm which can be grown in California. It is quite hardy, having several times withstood three successive nights of 20 degrees at the garden without injury. This palm will also endure desert or valley heat, as there are good specimens in Palm Springs and Indio. In Riverside, which is neither coast nor desert, but a bit of both, the *brandegeeis* look better than the *robustas*.

The fly in the ointment seems to be availability. There are many specimens in California; but they are widely scattered, although there are quite a few concentrated in Balboa Park, San Diego. The palm is easily grown from seed, and it seems little enough trouble to collect them and to sow them. If local sources are inadequate, Lower California is not very far away.

Native to Guadelupe Island off the west coast of Mexico, this is a slow-growing, absolutely upright, fan palm with a large head of very graceful, light-green foliage. It is similar in appearance in many ways to the Mexican blue, but has two very distinct advantages over this close relative. The leaves absciss by themselves, thus dispensing with the need for pruning, and the trunk, although slow to form, becomes smooth and grey underneath and is well-related to the spreading crown.

The Guadalupe palm also grows faster than the Mexican blue, putting on between 6 inches to 1 foot of growth per year in deep, rich, well-drained soil. In its native habitat specimens of 60 feet or more are known; but in the southwest coastal area 40 feet is probably the maximum height normally attained. In the desert, in good soil and with ample water and fertilizer this palm may grow to its full height.

The leaf stalks are broad but slender, usually unarmed, and are up to 5 feet long. The lower ones arch rather stiffly, giving an interesting character to the older leaves. The blades are 5 to 6 feet wide, often convex in the middle, producing a jaunty cant and trim appearance to the whole tree. The segments number about 70 and are deeply cut to one-third or one-half the blade length; when young they are covered with a woolly pubescence which later disappears. The branched flower spadix is heavily arched and may be 6 feet long; the yellow flowers are followed by chartreuse, turning-black, fruits. These hang down like large bunches of grapes, and are in striking contrast to the foliage. The fruits are freely borne —and equally freely dropped—a phenomenon this palm shares with the Mexican blue. Some people consider

this a nuisance for street or highway planting.

The Guadalupe palm can be grown throughout the range where most palms will grow, reaching its best development in coastal areas, and inland valleys. It does not grow well in the sandy soils of Palm Springs, but will stand the desert heat of Phoenix. It will endure occasional cold—down to 16° F. This palm may be grown from seed in the same way as the Mexican blue.

The Guadalupe palm should, and will be, much more widely planted to leaven the burden of the ubiquitous *Washingtonia robusta*. The foliage is fresh and green throughout the year, so that the rather grim winter aspect of the *Washingtonias* and some other fan palms in the moister coastal areas can be avoided. If the Guadalupe palm is used for streets or highways the seeds which take two years to mature may be inexpensively removed when they are still small. All *Erytheas* are hermaphrodites so that, unfortunately, this fruit problem cannot be solved by planting male trees.

Guadalupe palms make really excellent specimen trees: a group of two or more in the same hole will dominate and give character to a large area such as an entrance patio or a lawn (see photograph). They make marvelous fillers for shrub borders or planting boxes. After 5 years they can be planted out (or sold for much more than you paid for them).

Another *Erythea, E. elegans*, remains small, under 6 feet perhaps, and is even better for this purpose. In large groups this palm combines well with cacti, agaves, and other succulents. It seems to offer yet another shrub substitute for the landscape architect who is hard up for striking foliage material.

Guadalupe palm *in Phoenix, Arizona.*

There are many members of the genus Livistona, only a few of which are hardy. They are all natives of Australia and to eastern Asia. These fine palms are named in honor of Patrick Murray, Baron of Livingstone, who had a famous botanic garden near Edinburgh, Scotland, during the last century. As a genus they are particularly interesting, since several species are among the most widely used palms for indoor and greenhouse cultivation.

Livistona australis is native to eastern Australia. It is not uncommon in southern California and will grow as far north as San Francisco. It is easily recognized by its slender trunk and large round head of drooping leaves. As a young plant it is exceptionally beautiful with relaxed soft green foliage. Although a comparatively slow-grower, especially for the first few years, this palm will eventually reach 60 feet or more, as it often grows a foot a year once established.

The leaf blades are deeply cut to the middle or beyond into 40 or 50 narrow segments. The petioles are long and armed with spines. The flower stalk is curved, bearing greenish flowers and blue black fruits, which are almost hidden by the leaves.

Seeman, quoted in Nehrling, gives an interesting account of the palm's introduction into England. Apparently when Alan Cunningham, the King's Botanist, was in New Holland, he sent a case of living plants to the Royal Gardens at Kew, which, on being unpacked, was found to have, instead of the crocks usually placed at the bottom of such cases for drainage, seeds of a palm, nearly all in the process of germination. Cunningham's attendants, too indolent to look for the crocks, had substituted the seeds of *Livistona australis* which happened to be more handy. The young plants were carefully moved and one of them was later numbered among the gems of the palm collection at Kew.

Australian Fountain Palms like a moist heavy soil, rich in organic matter, as they are usually found in river valleys in their native haunts. They do not take kindly to sand, although, if protected from the hot sun during their early years, they will stand desert heat, for there are mature specimens in both Palm Springs and Phoenix. It is worth remembering that the leaves always look a more lustrous, glossy green in indirect light or shade. The palms are hardy to 20° F. or even 18° F. when they will sustain damage, but will usually recover if the sap is not up the tree. They are easily grown from seed in warm soil outside or heated beds in a greenhouse.

This Livistona should be much more widely planted in the Southwest as a substitute to *Washingtonia filifera*, to which, on the coast at least, it is a superior and more beautiful tree. Since the trunks are ultimately self-cleaning and the leaves are self-pruning, it makes a good avenue or street tree and looks well in lines or groups of any kind, because of its slenderness and fine proportions. As a young plant the Australian Fountain Palm is excellent in tubs or patios where its particular brand of beauty is most apparent.

Livistona australis (*left*) *and* Livistona decipiens.

The Chinese Fountain Palm is native to eastern Asia. This is another palm which is particularly beautiful in its younger state. Because of this it is widely grown as a pot, greenhouse, or indoor palm, where it is often wrongfully called *Latania borbonica.* It is slow to form a trunk, perhaps taking 10 years, and so is often used as a shrub-like cover under other palms and trees. The palm is used in this manner in the planter at the restaurant with the unusual roof at LaBrea and Sunset in Hollywood. Several Livistonas which I first remember seeing planted there in 1951 are still only 2-3 feet in height, although probably the conditions under which they are growing can hardly be considered optimum. After it takes off, the Chinese Fountain Palm will grow about 6 inches a year, reaching 20 to 30 feet eventually.

The head of this palm is large and globular. The trunk is smooth and ringed and seems slender by comparison. The bright green, shiny, rounded leaves are deeply cut into numerous segments. This accounts, in part, for the pendulous tips which give the fronds the appearance of a Christmas tree with icicles hanging down. The flowers are white; the fruits are blue and resemble olives.

The Chinese Fountain Palm is a clean tree. The old leaves stand out from the trunk and never form a shag. It is almost as hardy as the Australian Fountain Palm, down to 20° F. perhaps, but it does seem to prefer shade as a young plant and will definitely burn quite badly in full sun in the desert. In these circumstances its range might well be restricted to the coastal belt from Santa Barbara, south, and to inland valleys, if some relief from the mid-day sun is available. It is widely planted both in Florida and Hawaii. Like the other *Livistonas,* this palm prefers a deep, rich, moist, but well-drained, soil.

The Chinese Fountain Palm makes an excellent garden specimen, or it can be used in groups especially if backed by taller palms. The fountain-like effect of weeping heads is always interesting with dark and light green shrubs, like pittosporums and acacias, in the foreground. Older specimens make good lines or avenues.

In China, and elsewhere, the leaves are used for making the celebrated Chinese fans.

L. decipiens (see previous page) is a similar species to *L. australis,* but with a more slender trunk and a lighter, more graceful, head. The leaves droop most conspicuously at their ends and rustle delightfully in the slightest breeze, providing a psychological coolness on any summer's day. It is about as hardy as *australis.*

L. mariae was once considered a variety of *L. australis.* The plant is slow growing and hardy, but perhaps less so than the other two. It likes slightly acid soils and a moist climate. Its chief claims to fame are a more open, better articulated crown and the young leaves which are bright purplish-red in color. There are several fine specimens in the Los Angeles County Arboretum. The red Livistona palm was discovered in 1872.

L. rotundifolia is a tender palm which is popular in the tropics.

GRAHAM WARRINGTON

The generic name of the so-called Lady Palms is derived from the Greek "needle," referring, perhaps, to the shape of the leaves. To a landscape architect they are important as representing one of the very few hardy palms that are clump forming. They produce suckers at the base like the bamboos, which they superficially resemble. There are several superb clumps planted against the main buildings at the Huntington Botanic Garden. A well-grown *Rhaphis* is so graceful and such a wonderful composition in light and shadow that it has few rivals as a focal point in any garden design.

There are two species commonly grown in the Southwest, *Raphis humilis* and *excelsa*. Although they are both tough and have good garden constitutions, they need north light or shade for their best effect, as the leaves will yellow in full sun. Both *Raphis* are really fine pot or tub plants, for indoors, patio, or outdoors; and since they are amongst the hardiest of palms (down to 18° F.) they can be grown over a wide area, provided that they are under an overhang or patio roof protected from winds and storms, and that they are given rich, moist, but not wet, soil. From San Francisco to San Diego, on the coast and in inland valleys, they excel. They will grow in the desert, if given complete protection from the summer sun and syringed down now and again. They are magnificent in Florida and Hawaii.

Rhaphis humilis (right) is generally accepted to be the more attractive of the two species. Under exceptionally good conditions of light, rich soil and ample food and moisture, they may reach 18 feet—but half that height is more common. Outside, these palms will form dense clumps, many feet across, but they are among the best-behaved of container plants.

The leaves of *R. humilis* are in symmetrical, semi-circular fans, with 10 to 20 leaf segments. The dark green fans are deeply cut, and are like fingers. They are neatly borne by the slender reed-like stems, which are enveloped by dark, brown fibres, attached to the base of the leaves, and which, together with the leaves, give the plant a faintly sombre, almost brooding, aspect. These fibres may persist for years and during their tenure the plant is strongly oriental in appearance.

R. excelsa (*R. flabelliormis.* Shown in the photograph) is much smaller, perhaps growing to 5 feet, with thick, rather stiff stems, and 5 to 8 broad leaflets in the densely massed leaves, which are reminiscent of sasa bamboos. Although this species, too, likes shade, it will stand more sun than the preceding species.

Both species make the finest possible specimen shrubs in compositions or designs, where every element counts towards the total conception — the sort of landscape at which the Japanese have so long excelled. They look good with rocks, water, gravel and a few other plants in corners or in patios. They are fine in shrub borders, especially if protected and backed by a fence or the wall of a house. They combine wonderfully with bamboos, acanthus, *Chamaerops*, cycads, *Chamaedoreas*, and similar plants. A foreground of *Agapanthus*, day lilies, clivias, and crinums will add the finishing touch.

D. MUIRHEAD.

These are native palms of the U.S.A., Mexico, and the Caribbean. Within the U.S., they are found from the North Carolina coast south to Florida, and west to Texas. There are many different species; but as landscape subjects a lot of them are surprisingly similar, so that we can leave the confusion to the botanist. As a group, the tree sabals have the distinction of having leaves which are split down the middle, which is supposed to make them wind resistant. This is a distinct recognition feature. In addition, quite a few of them have trunks with a most attractive, basket-like weave caused by the old leaf bases.

Of the tree species *Sabal palmetto* is probably the best known. This palm forms huge stands in Florida, some of them containing thousands of plants, with individuals up to 80 feet tall, creating a most exciting landscape. They grow in a wide variety of soils and have been known to stand temperatures down to 15° F. The Palmetto does not do its best on the actual coast of California, since they need warm summers for a good growth. As a consequence most specimens look scrawny and ugly with age in this area. They look all right on the desert, though, in the few instances where I have seen them.

S. *umbraculifera* (shade-maker) is now the correct name for S. *blackburniana*, the stately palmetto of Bermuda. This palm is apparently the same species as the sabal growing in Haiti and San Domingo, which was named first and so has prior claim. The leaf stalks are 6 to 8 feet long and are curved, supporting a somewhat shorter, but very large, leaf of 40, or so, deeply cut leaflets. The flowers and black, shiny fruits, are borne among the fronds. In deep loam, with plenty of nitrogenous fertilizer and organic matter, this tree will reach 40 feet. Its trunk is heavy and columnar, and quite smooth of leaf bases. It will curve readily and adapts itself well to groups. The Bermuda palmetto will stand rough, tough conditions and will still grow into a good tree.

S. *exul* (see p 35), Victoria Palmetto. This is a really beautiful, straight-trunked tree, with a fine symmetrical head of erect and arching deep-green leaves. The basket-weave on the trunk is a really outstanding feature. Whenever I see this palm it looks trim and tidy, like some people whose clothes look smooth, even when they have been up all night. Fine specimens may be seen in the Huntington Botanic Garden. Botanists now recognize this palm as a variety of S. *texanum*, the Texas Palmetto. But to landscape architects it must remain a distinct species, which makes excellent groups, and by water, or on a patio, is pure garden sculpture. S. *exul* will grow slowly to 20 feet in 30 years. It is most handsome in all stages of growth.

S. *rosae* is a beautiful palmetto which provides the missing link between pinnate and palmate palms. It has a slender trunk and blue foliage.

S. *mexicana*, Mexican Palmetto, is a slow-growing plant of unusually tropical appearance, considering it is hardy to 15° F. It, too, is handsome in all stages of growth, and will remain dwarf for 10 years or more. It is very useful in groups in front of large bamboos or luxuriantly-foliaged trees, like *Firmiana simplex*, the hardy Chinese Parasol. A foreground of tree ferns or *Alocasias* will make a rich total composition.

S. *minor*, The Bush Palmetto, is a true dwarf sabal, which rarely forms a trunk. The leaves are bluish, deeply cut, 3 feet wide, borne on long straight petioles. The

Sabal minor

A fine stand of native palmettoes, Sabal palmetto in Florida.
Groups like this are not uncommon in many parts of the state.
Good groups of many other palms such as Washingtonia, dates and Guadalupes
can be made in a similar way.

effect obtained is rather like that of a rare greenhouse palm, which in California is striking and a trifle odd. Like the other Palmettos, the Bush Palmetto is a gross feeder and can hardly be fertilized too much. If Palmettoes do not get plenty of nitrogen their lower leaves turn yellow and die, looking quite unsightly while they do it. All Palmettos seem to do better where the summers are warm, preferring inland valleys and the desert (where they do very well, especially in Arizona) to the coastal strip, for which they are not recommended.

There are many other species of *Sabal,* but those mentioned above will fulfill all the requirements of the average landscape designer.

The young leaf shoots in the center of the Palmetto can be eaten; and Spaniards are reported to have kept alive on them for weeks in the early invasion of Florida. From this fact they derive their other name: the Cabbage Palm.

(Trachycarpus is Greek, meaning rough fruit, and the species is named for Robert Fortune, the famous English plant explorer who discovered it.)

This palm is native to China and probably to Japan, and has the undoubted distinction of being the hardiest palm which can be grown. Windmill palms had reached 28 feet in the temperate greenhouse at Kew, England before it was found they would also grow outside. One plant has withstood the winters of Edinburgh, Scotland, for 60 years (down to 5° F. and 10 inches of snow). Three were grown in the open in Beacon Hill Park, Victoria, Canada, for many years, where the first two succumbed to prolonged temperatures of between 0° and 10° F. There is still one left. The Windmill palm also grows in the cooler parts of the United States and has withstood minus 10° F. in Arkansas. It is quite common on the Oregon coast, where specimens 30 feet tall may be seen. In fact this palm seems to prefer the cooler coastal climates. The hotter it gets, the more ragged the palm looks and I have yet to see a good-looking specimen in the desert, where in my opinion it should not be grown.

The Windmill palm has a regular head of windmill-like fan-shaped leaves 3 feet or so across, deeply divided into numerous, rather stiff, dark-green leaflets. If the trunk is unpruned the old leaves will persist for many years. It is covered with black hairs which are produced from the sheathing bases of the leaves when they disintegrate. The flowers are large and yellow and are followed by masses of purplish grape-like fruits borne amongst the foliage.

The Windmill palm, oddly enough, is highly resistant to wind; and is often used by lakeshores or seacoasts. It is almost immune to insects and diseases.

Although it is extremely hardy and will grow wherever palms can be grown, this palm, not unnaturally, does not like low temperatures, nor storm-swept sites for preference, and a protected corner in colder climates will obviously pay off. On good sites it will grow 6 inches to a foot a year, reaching from 15 to 35 feet ultimately. It does not like loose gravel or sandy soils, and needs a heavy loam or clay and plenty of water, if the drainage is adequate, for its best growth. It responds markedly to liberal top dressings of manure.

As a landscape subject the Windmill palm makes a good street tree, and is effective in groups of different sizes as a cheaper substitute for *Chamaerops humilis*. It is also widely used as a tub or planting box palm and is extremely effective against white or pale pastel buildings.

OTHER SPECIES

T. martianus is similar to the Windmill palm, but is slower growing with a thinner trunk.

T. takil is also slow-growing but has most beautiful foliage and is very effective as a young plant.

Windmill palm at Los Angeles County Arboretum, Arcadia, California. Row of robus- *tas in background shows varying degrees of shag-shedding due to wind (see pages 41, 43)*

Native to the United States from South Carolina to Alabama, Georgia, and Florida. This low, shrubby palm is the American equivalent of *Chamaerops humilis* and once bore the name *C. hystrix*. It will grow approximately 10 feet wide and 6 or more feet high in 20 years; it is hardy to at least 18° F. but has reportedly stood −5° F. in Arkansas.

The generic name means "needle leaf" and the specific name, "porcupine," refers to the black, needle-like spines which jut out from the fibrous trunk. This is nature's way of protecting the flowers. These spines are not such a problem as those of *Trithrinax* however, since the trunks, and indeed the flowers and fruit, are completely covered with densely-packed, 3 to 4 foot long, shiny leaves which are silver beneath, and which together form a fine clump of considerable beauty. The excellent specimens in the Huntington Botanic Garden give a clue to the landscape possibilities of this shrub, which (once it is more available) may become unlimited. It is especially suitable for some of the more extreme forms of contemporary architectural gardens. The Needle palm likes a rich, moist soil, since it grows in swamps and limestone pockets in its native haunts. This palm does exceedingly well on the Pacific Coast and should prove satisfactory for shrub borders wherever palms are grown.

Trithrinax acanthocoma (See drawing). A native of southern Brazil, this tree has the best shaped and sculptured leaf of any hardy fan palm. It stands temperatures down to 18° F. without injury and can be grown in all zones from the coast to the desert.

The leaves are large, stiff, dark green and very regular. They are deeply cut, almost to their bases, into 40 or so narrow folded segments. On careful inspection, it will be seen that each leaf is split into three individual fans, as the generic name suggests. The hermaphrodite flowers are borne laterally in clusters, like bunches of hazel catkins. They are very light, against the dark green leaves, and are consequently quite striking. They are followed by yellow-green fruits. The trunk, which may reach 12 to 15 feet and is stiffly upright, is covered with numerous strong, light-brown spines which are sharp, rigid, and several inches long. Although they are by no means ugly, these spines preclude the use of this palm in public places where children may suffer from contact with it. As a backing for a billowy mass of shrubbery, however, *Trithrinax* is fine. It also looks good with all kinds of desert planting. This palm is also appropriate in all types of architectural gardens.

Trithinax acanthacoma

Raphidophyllum hystrix *and* Sabal exul.

T. campestris is a dwarf, slow-growing palm from Argentina. It is very handsome and makes a fine clump—so it can be used as a shrub in the garden. The young leaves are tomentose, appearing white from above.

The only palm native to western U.S.A., the California fan palm is found in a few canyons and draws in southwestern Arizona and southeastern California. It is the characteristic palm of Palm Canyon and Twentynine Palms near the burgeoning resort community of Palm Springs, where it grows in dense stands with a shag, or skirt, of old leaves often reaching to the ground. For this reason it is known in Hawaii as the hula palm.

For some time a controversy has raged amongst landscape architects and others whether this skirt should be retained in the cultivated specimens of this palm, which is used as an

ornamental in every subtropical country in the world. Anyone who has seen the nobility and dignity of the wild trees standing amidst the boulders and clear water of Palm Canyon will question the act of pruning this skirt. However, in the trim surroundings of gardens and city streets, alas, it is strangely out of place and, worse still, it harbors scorpions and other vermin, and is a fire hazard. Recently a man was suffocated when an entire skirt slipped down the trunk and enveloped him while he was attempting to prune it. Obviously the California fan palm must have this shag removed, preferably annually; and, in my opinion, it is still a handsome tree of great dignity and character and exceptionally even growth. The older streets of Phoenix, Arizona, which are planted exclusively to this tree, are some of the finest and most impressive tree-lined streets in the world.

Specimens of this palm, both in the wild and in cultivation, have been known to reach 100 feet in height and more than 100 years of age. Under normal conditions of good soil and plentiful water (it grows naturally by water courses, remember, and loves lake shores or canal banks) it will grow better than a foot a year to an average height of about 60 feet. The trunks are dead-straight, wide, and heavy, with vertical and horizontal wrinkles resembling elephants feet and legs. The head is fine and large, with glistening green leaves up to 6 feet wide with 40 to 70 segments deeply cut to one-half or two-thirds of the length of the blade. Numerous thread-like filaments hang from the margins of the segments. The leaf stalks are stout and 3 to 5 feet long, armed with broad, hooked spines. The black, shiny fruits are profusely borne and were once eaten by the Indians. They burned the trees to increase the crop, thus many of the wild trees are fire-blackened by man or by nature. Strangely enough, this did not harm them, since, like all palms, they have no true cambium or bark, just conducting vessels scattered through the trunk. The Indians also ate the buds (thus killing the trees), made a sort of flour from the seeds, and obtained thatch and utensils from the leaves.

The *filifera* is quite hardy, down to

A magnificent street of filifera *palms in Phoenix, Arizona. These trees, if planted at the same time, make a remarkably even growth.*

at least 15° F., but is less so as a small plant when it will "burn" a bit at any temperature less than 25° F. It does not look too good on the coast and in addition it is subject to a fatal fungus there. It certainly should not be planted in the San Francisco Bay region where it invariably looks miserable and ratty. This noble palm looks its best in the desert and even in Las Vegas, Globe, or Nogales it will grow thriftily, if slowly. The *filifera* is easily propagated by seed. In desert regions any moist flower beds or compost heaps near an old tree will be covered with young seedlings which can be moved into the garden if needed.

Filifera palms have numerous uses in the landscape, in groves, in lines or in avenues. Their columnar forms mean that even a few palms will have a telling effect on the space around them. They make magnificent groups and can be formed in patterns, circles, angles, and lines with other trees most effectively. Two or three palms at random in front gardens will give a whole street character. They also make tough and reliable tub plants as long as they are replaced when they get too big, due to their fast growth.

(Above) A group of robustas *near the pool of the Paradise Valley Racquets* **Club**, **Phoenix**, *Arizona. These trees were moved in full size.*

(Left) A superb group of filiferas *on a golf course in the Arizona desert.*

(Above) Another view of a Phoenix street, note the columnar regularity of the trunks.

(Right) A row of robustas in Scottsdale, Arizona relieving the monotony of the stores. To see how they look without trees put your index finger over the palms.

40

WASHINGTONIA ROBUSTA

Mexican fan palm. Robusta

Standardized plant names has given this palm the cumbersome soubriquet of Mexican Washington Palm. This teeth-rattling mouthful, fortunately, has not been accepted by the trade, where the tree is known simply as "robusta"; and in the wayward manner of botanical nomenclature you can remember it since it is much less robusta than the *filifera!*

A very slender-trunked tree with a flared base, it rockets skywards to a quite small, dainty head of leaves. As in the *filifera*, the shag is persistent and should be removed. As the sailor said, there are occasionally instances where a long skirt looks right: perhaps in the group in the little cactus park just past Rodeo on Santa Monica Boulevard in Hollywood, California. Another instance where it does *not* is on the main terrace outside the Huntington Art Gallery in San Marino where the unkept, scurvy effect is in uncomfortable contrast to the beautifully manicured lawns, balustrades, and paving materials. As the tree grows and becomes subject to high winds, half the shag will be blown off, leaving the unattractive chicken-leg trunks so common round Riverside, California.

41

GRAHAM WARRINGTON

*(Above) Handsome full-foliaged groups of even-sized robus-
tas reduce the tedium of a parking area. (Below) Robustas
shaggy, pruned, with a clump and with a random arrangement like coconuts.*

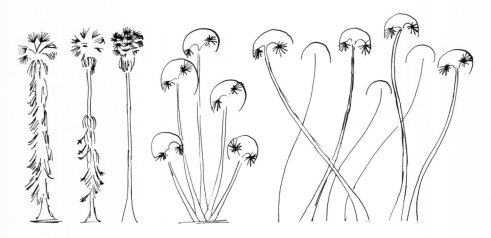

As well as height, thickness of trunk and size of crown, W. *robusta* can be distinguished from W. *filifera* by shorter leaf stalks (2 to 3 feet), less deeply divided leaves (one-third the length of the leaf blade) and petioles armed with spines for their entire length. W. *filifera* has spines for only one-half its length. Small plants are, however, hard to tell apart because of hybridisation.

This tree is one of the commonest palms in the West, due perhaps to its astonishing vigor. Provided the drainage is good, it will respond to liberal manuring, fertilizing, and watering to the tune of 2 feet plus per year, ultimately reaching 100 feet or more. If the drainage is perfect, the robusta will take all the water you can give it, growing sometimes 6 feet a year. Large specimens may be seen in rows from most of the Los Angeles freeways. It is also the characteristic palm of the township of Palm Springs.

The clean, graceful form of this palm is very effective in helping to translate tall buildings to the human scale of the passer-by. It also makes fine avenues, excellent rows (see page 5), and can be used in groups, circles or groves. Clumps are very fine, but are best with robustas of different sizes like the Tropicana in Las Vegas, or the new plantings in the central islands on Wilshire Boulevard in Los Angeles. Large trees can be twisted and angled like coconuts, although smaller trees will tend to turn upright from their initial slanted positions.

With age the groups may look rather odd. As the palm reaches maturity the head often looks too small for the long straight trunk. If so, sell the largest palm or palms (they move very easily), and plant some small ones at the base.

Robustas are valuable. You may get $4 to $10 per foot for them. They retail for $7.00 to $20.00 a foot, depending on size, condition and transport distance.

Single, tall robustas may look uncomfortable by relatively small homes. Pluck up courage and take them out if they look old, awkward, or unhappy. A classic case of robustas outgrowing their position may be seen in the garden of the antique store in Beaumont, California, where six robustas planted in a circle 'round a little formal garden about 12 feet in diameter are now at least 50 feet high and dominate the whole town.

Hardy to 15° F. the robusta will grow throughout the Southwest, Florida and Hawaii. But it does like heat and looks its best under desert conditions. This palm is now being grown in the millions, especially in Texas, and is being used in scads by promoters to ensure their clientele that the area of their motel or housing development has a tropical climate, often when more suitable or more refined trees could do a better job. But used properly as a small or large tree the robusta is an asset to the landscape and is grown in all the countries of the world where it is hardy.

Washingtonia X robusta. W. *robusta* and W. *filifera* hybridise freely, producing marvelous trees with the best qualities of both parents. They are more slender than *filifera* but with larger heads than robusta — more like *Livistonas*, perhaps. They make really excellent groups not likely to look uncomfortable eventually like mature robustas, and are better street trees. As far as I know no nursery is growing them but often large trees are available from palm specialists.

THE HARDY FEATHER PALMS

All except the *Chamaedoreas* are hardy to at least 18° F.

ARECASTRUM ROMANZOFFIANUM

[Cocos plumosa]

Queen Palm

This is undoubtedly one of the commonest palms in southern California and yet it is one of those trees which can be either a delightful addition to the landscape or an eyesore. San Diego is full of Queen palms, many of which are planted in *caliche* holes on the street. Not more than 10 percent look really well-grown, the rest display various aspects of neglect — from a rather shaggy despond to downright tiredness. In Pasadena a few variously-sized, unhappy specimens struggle in vain on Colorado Ave., the main street of the city. It is likewise in many parts of Los Angeles. And yet in the San Fernando Valley where there is rich deep soil and the water table is only 3 or 4 feet below the surface, the Queen palm often makes a magnificent showing, with a luxurious head of arching fronds on a fine, straight, silvery bole. There are many good plants in Santa Barbara, too, although specimens on slopes by bridges on the freeways look starved and stunted. This is probably due to inadequate water and competition from the ivy ground covers.

Obviously the Queen palm requires good deep soil (or an equivalent planting hole), adequate drainage, and unlimited water. If you give it this, it will be a credit to you. If you can't, don't plant it in the first place.

A native of Brazil, where it is known as the Pindo palm, the Queen palm is easily recognized by its 10 or more arched, feathery leaves, like ostrich plumes. These may be stiff and ascending, or curved and drooping, with variations in between.

A. romanzoffianum var. *botryophorum*, for instance, is bigger and stronger in all its parts and should be distributed instead of the current variety in the trade. The pinnae of all varieties are long and narrow and are often broken at the ends. The flowers are yellow and the fruits are orange.

Under good conditions the Queen palm will reach 40 feet in 30 years. It is not a long-lived tree and does not like smog. (Who does?) It is hardy to at least 18° F. but young plants are often injured at 25° F. Temperatures of 112° F. or more will burn the fronds, which also go yellow if the water is too alkaline. This can be cured by the application of magnesium sulfate or chelated iron. Sometimes an application of nitrogenous fertilizer will help them through. As with all palms, organics are preferred to chemicals. I have seen beautiful Queen palms in Palm Springs, Phoenix, and Tucson, but if they don't have good soil, food, and plenty of water, specimens in the sun have looked rough, those in the wind have looked terrible, and only sheltered or shaded specimens have looked healthy. In the desert, Queen palms either need the protection of other trees, where they sometimes provide an interesting change of foliage texture, or they should be planted on the north sides of fairly tall buildings, where, to be truthful, they look strangely out of place. Besides the Pacific Coast and the desert the Queen palm is also grown in Florida and in Hawaii.

Queen palms make excellent groups spaced 10 or more feet apart. They

*Santa Barbara, California. Young Queen palm
in excellent condition because of plentiful
fertilizer and water supply.*

should never be planted on a slant or in the same hole, since their heads and foliage clash. If largish trees of the same size are selected (especially var. *botryophorum*), they will make good avenues in coastal regions or wherever citrus groves are common, but if small trees are used the result is liable to be quite uneven, as the palm is so variable.

A well-grown Queen palm is a most satisfying plant, as the picture shows. A poorly grown one is an insult to any self-respecting landscape.

45

Known in the trade as *Cocos australis*, the butia palm is a native of Brazil and Uruguay. It has also been called jelly palm, since the fruits, which may be in clusters weighing 75 pounds or more, are used for making jelly. The product, incidentally, is available in some U. S. stores. The fruit, by a quirk of nature, smells like a pineapple.

This is a strong, tough tree, which in Pacific coastal areas and in Florida pinelands withstands the most difficult conditions of heat and drought of any palm — although it needs plenty of water and care to make a good specimen on the hot desert. It is hardy to 12° F. (at least as an old plant), and is uninjured when citrus trees are badly damaged, even killed. On occasions butias have been known to survive when date palms have been destroyed by frost.

This is another palm which has leaf bases that are very persistent. They are light grey, in vertical rows and I, personally, do not find them ornamental. If these leaf bases are removed the result is smooth and more attractive.

The trunk is short and very slow-growing to about 10 feet; but the large lush head is effective as a landscape subject even with small plants. The fronds are heavily arched and recurved, like mammoth tusks; but the foliage, although long, blue and fiercely pointed, is surprisingly harmless when touched. The blue color and the pinnate leaves easily identify the palm.

The butia palm looks its best with a dark green background, such as *Magnolia grandiflora,* holly, or Carolina cherry laurel, where its silvery blueness really comes to life. It should be used in groups, spaced 10 or so feet apart, and clumps of two or more should never be planted in the same hole, since the head is too big for this. If the trunks are not smooth, a foreground of pittosporum or *Cassia splendida* will produce a magnificent effect. There are some good groups of butias near the entrance to the zoo at Balboa Park in San Diego.

Butias will make good lawn specimens; but they must receive perfect grooming. Old leaves must be removed immediately, or the result is liable to be grotesque and odd, rather than beautiful.

Butias are not long-lived palms. Their natural span does not usually exceed 30 to 40 years. They are handsome trees, if properly used, but as a rule they have been unwisely planted in the past. One possible drawback to them is that they do not combine well with other palms. They need lots of lush foliage like citrus, magnolias or pines to prevent their dominating the space to an almost ridiculous extent. Sabals and butias must never be planted together. They are both prima-donna forms which squabble and fight, resulting in a restless grouping.

Due to its toughness the butia makes an excellent tub plant, thus providing a method which may facilitate its landscape arrangement for those who are unhappy with it as a garden plant.

There are many other species of *Butia* which are hard to tell apart, so that *B. capitata* is an adequate representative of the group for purposes of landscape design, although *B. yatay* has a taller trunk and more graceful foliage as a young plant.

Young Butia palm beginning to form trunk.

This is a beautiful dwarf, hardy palm which is grown throughout the world as an indoor pot plant. Its popularity as an outdoor palm is now increasing on the Pacific coast, where it will withstand temperatures down to 25° F. Temperatures of 20° F. will kill it to the ground; but as the photograph shows, this palm will come back stronger than ever in a dense clump. The palm illustrated had withstood two lots of three successive nights of 20° F., spaced 12 years apart. At Riverside, California plants covered with a burlap cylinder withstood 18° F. and remained unharmed.

Collinia elegans and, indeed, most *Chamaedorea* species need full shade to do their best, against a north wall, under patio roofs, or in tubs. Here unlike many plants they will not lean towards the nearest source of light but will grow upright. They will reach, eventually, 6 to 10 feet in height. Their foliage is fresh and shimmering green with clear, green stems, like bamboos. As patio and tub plants they can be grown throughout the southwest, Florida and Hawaii.

Since they are jungle plants they prefer moist climates. In hot desert climates they should be syringed down daily. On the coast, they will stand more light but will tend to go yellow if they are not shaded from the midday sun. They will not, however, be otherwise harmed.

Fine specimens of *Collinia* can be seen at the Huntington Botanic Garden and on the shaded side of buildings at the Los Angeles County Arboretum. It is an excellent landscape subject, used much in the same way as bamboo. With a foreground of acanthus or other bold foliage, or with flowers like begonias, *Collinias* will make a fine picture.

Neanthe bella, the popular dwarf indoor palm, is considered a young or juvenile form of *C. elegans.*

For indoor planting or pot planting all palms are usually provided with a special soil mix, although *Howeas* will grow in practically any soil which is adequately supplied with peat or similar organic matter. We have found that *Chamaedoreas, Chrysalidocarpus,* fish tails, etc., do best in a mixture as follows:

> 3 parts good loam topsoil (preferably rotted turf)
> 1½ parts peat
> 1½ parts dried cow manure
> 1½ parts sand
> ½ cup bone meal, two cups charcoal, to each peck of mixture.

Planting boxes and tubs must be supplied with good drainage. At least 3 inches of coarse gravel or broken flower pots. Scales may be a problem. If they are not removed the plant will look untidy and unhappy. A contact insecticide will look after them, when young. Later on, when they are mature, they may be washed off, using a sponge and soapy water.

The chief problems of patio or indoor plants is one of watering. Most palm fronds appreciate being washed down or sprayed once a day and a deep soaking for the entire plant once a week. In extensive indoor plantings or on desert patios an automatic atomizer is advised and will soon pay for itself.

CHAMA

GRAHAM WARRINGTON

Collinea elegans *in full sun at the Huntington Botanic Garden.*

There are numerous specimens of *Chamaedorea,* all from the humid rain forests of Mexico and Central and South America, where they grow usually in deep shade. They are found in moist leaf mould on the valley floor — which should give the key to their cultivation in the United States. They like a rich moist soil in a shaded location: under a patio roof, an overhang or a tree which does not make the soil underneath it too dry.

CHAMAEDOREA COSTA-RICANA
Costa Rica Palm

A stooling plant which will replace the bamboo in shade, as, like *Collinia,* it does not grow towards the light but grows upright; nor does it drop its foliage like most bamboos. The stems are green and shining with white clasping leaf bases which are most ornamental. The leaves curve elegantly away from the stems. This plant is a landscape architect's dream, filling practically every requirement of a handsome structural shrub for a variety of uses. It will make good clumps, groups, or single specimens in patios, or next to walls or building. It is an excellent plant for containers. It has the same universal quality as bamboo for combining with other plants. Acanthus, ferns, tree ferns, aspidistras, clivias, elephant ears, cycads, fatsias, fuchsias, iteas, etc., all make fine groups with this palm, and if there is enough light in front to include some golden stemmed bamboos, some flowers or foliage plants like dusty miller, the greenness of the grouping is relieved.

C. *costa-ricana* will not usually exceed 10 feet in height. It is hardy to 25° F., or throughout the Southwest in shaded, sheltered locations. It is also a good indoor plant. There are some fine specimens in pots in the patio at the new Bullock's store in Santa Ana.

C. GEONOMIFORMIS
(see inset above)

A native of Guatamala is interesting mainly because its leaves are shaped like *Geonoma,* the tropical palm, which is frost tender. These broad wedge-shaped leaves are deeply cut at the end of the wedge with a vee-shaped cut, providing a landscape subject of impressive form and texture, like a combination of bamboo and fatsia.

C. ERNESTII-AUGUSTII
(See inset)

A native of Mexico similar to the above, but with much larger leaves.

C. GRAMINAEFOLIA

This is a representative of those *Chamaedoreas* with the narrow pinnae and glaucous foliage; it will take more light than most, even full sun. There are numerous other *Chamaedoreas,* all of which are good landscape subjects. The above selections I consider the best, but they are all worthy of a trial in coastal gardens, in inland patios and in their native tropics. Most of them are hardy to 25° F., as are all of those discussed above. They are propagated either by seed or by division. This process should be performed in warm weather or in a greenhouse in the winter months. Saw the plant in several pieces, making vertical cuts. If *Chamaedoreas* get too tall, do not cut them back, but prune the offending canes right out.

Chamaedorea costa-ricana

The Chilean Wine Palm is native to the west Andean slopes in Chile, where it grows into a massive tree of great nobility. Although there are still large stands there, Darwin in his famous book, "Voyage of the Beagle," recalls an estate where hundreds of thousands were cut down for the sap. This is collected from the crown of the tree, is boiled to make a syrup, and, ultimately, when fermented, a delicious brew. This wasteful process must have destroyed many fine groves; but the Indians also obtained lumber, baskets, brooms, thatch, and many other materials from the trees.

Named for Juba, King of Numidia, who was reputed to have a great interest in botany, the Chilean Wine Palm has an enormous columnar trunk, 5 feet or more in diameter, and 60 feet high when mature. There are many fine specimens in Santa Barbara and Riverside, California, where a few trees have already reached these proportions, although they are no more than 50 years old. The bark is corky and is arranged in a bizarre pattern of narrow, sculptured diamonds, which, together with the large size, readily identify the tree. The foliage head is dense, and forms an almost perfect hemisphere. In the tropics, if the picture on page 156 of McMillan's book "Tropical Planting and Gardening" is accurate, the head is enormous and lushly drooping. In temperate regions the leaves, which appear shorter than those of many feather palms, are stiff with little curvature. The segments are convex, hanging down in regular tiers from the central midrib. The leaf stalk is unarmed. The flowers are produced on long spathes and the fruit hangs in clusters. The individual nuts are called *coquites*, or little coconuts, by the Chileans, and are a source of vegetable oil.

The leaves are quite small in young plants: perhaps as little as 3 feet, and faintly uncomfortable in appearance. As the tree starts growing a trunk at the rate of almost a foot or so a year, they become larger, perhaps eventually reaching 15 feet in length.

Altogether, this fine palm is a tree of great character. A large specimen in a park or garden will completely dominate the scene it surveys, like a great actor commanding the stage by his presence. Because of its magnificence in old age, this tree should be widely planted. It does well throughout the warm temperate zone from San Francisco south (there is a good specimen in Golden Gate Park), and in the desert, with a hardiness about equivalent to the Canary Island Date. Bean reports a tree 45 feet high and 10 feet in girth in the temperate house at Kew, England, where it has been successfully grown outside in the past. In other parts of Europe *Jubaeas* have withstood temperatures of 10° F., which is not surprising since they are found the farthest south of any American palm species.

Mature specimen of Jubaea.

This, one of the commonest ornamental trees in Southern California, is a native of the Canary Islands where it is found in large numbers, and where a grove of these trees with their dark green fronds against bright green turf is a sight to remember. Moreover, it is not only one of the cleanest, tidiest, and most impressive palms which can be grown, but is also one of the toughest and hardiest, enduring temperatures down to 12° F. and growing well from north of San Francisco (there are fine specimens in Union Square) throughout central and southern California and the warm desert regions of the U.S. It is, incidentally, equally at home on the Gulf Coast, in Florida, or in Hawaii.

In the desert the Canary Island Date does particularly well in Tucson, where there is an excellent avenue at the Veteran's Hospital. The finest specimens, however, are found on the coast in Santa Barbara; especially on the Hope Ranch, and on the coast road leading north from the town, and in Hollywood and Beverly Hills. There are many well-grown trees in the older section of La Jolla, where this palm is used extensively as an avenue tree, giving the whole area a magnificence quite out of proportion to the commonplace, if innocuous, architecture. Modern subdividers should take note. For an expenditure of $10.00 a lot they could eventually ensure an area of fabulous beauty, and of stately dignity, with two glorious trees in each garden. In time perhaps (or is it too much to hope?) they would completely hide the houses.

Although the Canary Island Date grows into a large tree often 60 feet tall and 3 or 4 feet in diameter, this is a 100-year proposition and, in most cases, it will only grow 6 inches to a foot per year. The Beverly Hills area is perhaps an exception, where some especially tall specimens may be seen. Certainly it is a fit subject for subdivisions, in spite of the literature to the contrary. Large masses of other foliage such as citrus, *Ficus*, jacarandas, eucalyptus, *Albizzia* and palo verde will help tone down the powerful aura of this tree. These other trees will help translate it to a more human scale, and, consequently, to a quieter landscape, if this is desired. This palm is a particularly nice tree to look down on from upper story windows, since from above the fronds are unusually fresh and glistening.

The Canary Island Date has leaves which are up to 15 feet long, numbering perhaps 100 or more, which cumulatively form a large, globular crown on a straight, erect trunk. The pinnae are a dark, glossy green. The tree is a gross feeder and likes plenty of water; in other words, our old friend, a rich, moist soil. Under these conditions, it is as sleek and smooth as a race horse and you could not believe this was the same tree which survives, admittedly, on all soil types, and will also stand wind and sea spray, which has made it into a popular sea front or marina tree. Canary Island Dates, like most other large palms, will stand heavy mulching with manure and regular applications of 10-15 pounds of strong commercial fertilizer, applied two to three times a year, especially if the leaves are yellowing. This should be applied over the area of the foliage on the ground. Larger amounts may be needed if the tree is growing in a lawn. If the foliage is still yellow, a nutritional spray applied in March should be tried.

The tree will prune itself in time, leaving large leaf bases, but it looks better if the dead leaves are biennially, or annually, cut clean with a saw; a really good job produces a rich-textured trunk, with a wonderful, blunted-diamond pattern. This is the familiar diamond trim. Stubs of the more recently dead leaves are often left 6 inches long and cut later, producing a rather unusual-looking bulge beneath the foliage crown. They can, however, and probably should, be cut close, like the rest of the tree.

The fruit is borne on spadices 6 feet or more in length, on female trees only, since all the date palms are monoecious. The clusters are orange and enormous, and present a terrific sight against the dark green leaves. The fruit is considered edible; but so are cats in some societies. The dark green leaves, their heavy curvature, the dense crown, and massive trunk fortunately make confusion with the true date palm close to impossible.

The Canary Island Date should be widely planted in avenues, along roadsides and driveways, and in groups. It looks very good with *robustas*, pines, or *Eucalyptus citriodora* behind and *Acacia longifolia* and other spreading evergreen shrubs in front. It makes an excellent fern-like tub plant as a young tree, tough and undemanding, resembling a large pineapple as the trunk begins to grow. The small palm can be later set out in the garden.

Santa Barbara, California, has an excellent variety of complementary tree species. Other cities should try planting three or four different types in large numbers. Here are Canary Island Dates, Eucalyptus citriodora, Monterey cypress, and Monterey pine.

JOSEF MUENCH

The date is thought to be the tree of life of the Bible. Many millions of people live on this tree alone, dates and water not only comprising their principal diet but also feeding their stock. Besides this, the date was used for several hundred different purposes in Persia and Babylon, where it probably originated as a wild tree, and where even today life in the date groves has changed little in nearly 7000 years. Date beams, for instance, are used for posts and for roof construction and date leaf stems for fuel and for furniture; the leaves themselves are used for thatch and fencing, for needles, thread and baskets. On feast days the date also provides an intoxicating liquor, Arak; for this old palms are employed, an incision being made beneath the flower to extract the sap. Latterly, the leaves have been used in many parts of the world for Palm Sunday.

The date spread eventually to East Pakistan on the one hand and to Egypt, Spain, and Morocco, on the other. In time it was established in many other countries where the climate was suitable: in places as far apart as Queensland in Australia, and Arizona and California in the United States. As an ornamental, the date has spread even further, to all the warm temperate and tropical regions of the world; but this does not mean dates are produced on these trees. For this, special conditions are necessary.

The town of Basra in Iraq lies at the confluence of the historic Tigris and Euphrates and, from here, the mighty yellow waters of the two rivers, now joined, flow down to the Persian gulf. This last river is known as the Shatt-Al-Arab and around it lie many acres of rich, flat, silt land, easily irrigated. The temperatures are in the hundreds for several months, the air is dry and there is cool weather in the winter. The trees have "their heads in the fire, their feet in the water," so the conditions are ideal for date production. In this compact area, only a few miles wide, there are estimated to be 20 million trees. It is by far the greatest date growing area in the world, and practically every other region where dates are grown commercially bears points of striking similarity to this valley.

The site of the main date growing area in the United States is no less arresting. Driving from Desert Center towards Palm Springs you climb up through innumerable gravel cuts bordered by scattered tufts of silver brittle bush, olive greasewood and dark green ocotillo. Suddenly you emerge into a dazzling scene of vast sun-drenched space. A thousand feet below you is the valley of the Coachella, with endless blocks and groves of date and citrus, counterpointed with long hedges of oleander and tamarisk and with lines of Bauhinia trees. It is a landscape of noble scale and proportion which shames the mediocre urban sprawl of Palm Springs, Phoenix, Tucson and other desert cities. It is one of the great sights of America.

The dates grown around Indio, mainly of the Algerian Deglet Noor variety, are the sweetest I have ever tasted, and, undoubtedly, the cleanest, as all who have traveled in Arab countries will verify. No one who has visited these dark groves is left unawed by the magnificence of the scene around him, as rough, massive, columnar forms thrust skywards to the delicately textured canopy of grey-green fronds. The repetition of this powerful sculpture is moving and a little sombre, like a huge, beautiful cumulo-nimbus cloud about to shut out the sun on a dark day.

The scene is marred only by the billboards, still the shame of the Amer-

Huge old date palms near the 300-feet-high bell tower of the cathedral of Cordoba, Spain.

ican countryside, except in Massachusetts where a law now regulates them, and in Hawaii where a band of 2500 vigilant women has kept them out. A large crude sign announcing a movie, "The Romance and Sex Life of the Date," reminds you that primitive people worshiped the tree because of its strange sexual process.

In those days the priest would walk down the grove solemnly, waving stalks of the male flowers and thus unconsciously pollenizing the female trees. Such overwhelming magic con-

An orchard of well-pruned dates at Indio, California. Alternate rows have been removed.

vinced the people of many nations and manifested itself eventually in their art and literature.

Unfortunately, even with the potent help of an interesting sex life, the date industry has only thrived in this country in wartime, when cheaper, imported dates, were unavailable. The industry has been plagued by high capital outlay, high labor costs and low prices. Despite the excellent food value of the date and the fine quality of the local product, it has never really found acceptance here, and nowadays there are more groves which are being converted to subdivisions than planted for fruit. The subdivisions in the date groves, incidentally, are some of the most attractive in the Southwest, especially where they are interplanted with citrus.

Those wanting to recreate a date grove around their houses, a laudable performance in all desert areas, and one which will increase the value of the property immensely, may be interested in some vital statistics. The date is propagated by offshoots which appear at the base of the trunk and which, after 4 or 5 years, have produced roots. They are removed in periods of warm weather, in late spring or summer, with a large chisel. Then their lower leaves are stripped, and the upper ones cut back. They are planted in basins 6 feet across and 6 inches deep to facilitate irrigation. The preferred planting distance is 30 by 30 feet, which makes about 48 trees to the acre, although in windy or colder areas they are planted as close as 15 feet apart, or 200 to the acre. In the burning winds of the Basra area, they are planted 10 feet apart for mutual protection.

A high water table is always good since the roots of the date are deep. In certain areas where the water table is only a few feet below the surface, they will get by without irrigation; but where it is much more than 5 or 6 feet, they will live, but only just, and will not fruit. The type of soil, too, is obviously important in determining the amount of irrigation. A heavy soil that contains about 35 per cent water at field capacity will obviously hold several times as much water as a light sandy soil which may have trouble holding any water. After planting, the offshoots are irrigated twice a week for the first year or two. Heavy soils are irrigated twice a month in summer, getting 5 acre inches per irrigation. This is reduced to once or less per month in winter. Light soils may need as much as double this amount of water.

The date is, however, a xerophytic plant with superb adaption of trunk and leaf to withstand water loss. It will get by for many seasons without water as any visit to an abandoned date orchard will confirm.

Animal manure supplemented by nitrogen is used to fertilize the dates, which are heavy feeders, in any soil type. A tree in good condition should produce 10 to 14 leaves per year and over 100 pounds of fruit.

Pruning consists of annual removal of dead leaves in the winter, and of the spines on the leaf stems before pollenation and picking. Wind pollenation will usually ensure a crop in the garden, but hand pollenation, where strands of flowers from the male tree are placed across the female flowers, is necessary in commercial orchards. The fruit is normally thinned for maximum size and quality. Even so, the bunches ripen irregularly and artificial ripening in moist packing cases at high temperatures is recommended.

Most good date areas have low rainfall, since the fruit easily rots in moist summers, and often needs protection by paper bags even in the driest climates. The first crop is usually obtained 6 years after planting. Ten years after planting you may get 50 pounds per tree per year; the crop should increase annually after this.

Once established, the date palm will stand a terrific range of heat and cold. Fire can blacken the trunk and burn all the leaves off, but the tree will not die. Conversely, it is one of the most resistant palms to low temperatures. In the U. S. Department of Agriculture date garden at Indio, the thermometer hit 13° F. one black night in January 1937 and hovered around the 18° F. to 20° F. mark for several hours for two nights running. It appears that the date, like most hardy palms, would stand 20° F. without injury, but that anything below this produced severe damage. Younger trees were the worst affected, since the higher the tree, the less cold the air. Many trees were completely defoliated; but amazingly few died. This is probably because of the leaf arrangement. Date phyllotaxy shows 13 leaves in a whorl, providing a mass of fibre and leaf stalks, giving the bud, or growing point, much protection.

If further information is required on the date as a cultivated crop, "Growing Dates in the United States," by Roy W. Nixon, obtainable from the U. S. Department of Agriculture, Indio, California, is filled with good stuff.

I have already mentioned that the date groves make magnificent sites for both city or subdivision. The date is also an excellent avenue tree, by itself, or combined with citrus, one date to two citrus, or even intermingled with citrus and other trees. The silver-leaved varieties and the hybrid with *P. zeylanica,* which have leaves the color of Kosters' blue spruce, are the most attractive. This latter is a most ornamental date species. So is *P. sylvestris,* the Indian Date Palm, which has softer, more pliant fronds, and which looks quite distinctly East Indian in appearance.

In small groves, or groups, dates should be planted upright (see page 59). Leaning palms planted in pairs, such as those on some desert golf courses, have heads too big to look well so close together; they may look rather grand in time, like the old dates in Egypt whose off-shoots have not been removed, but they could take 20 years to do it, and will probably turn upright as they grow, anyway.

Deglet Noors particularly have beautiful trunks if about 6 inches of leaf base is left (see photograph, page 59). These leaf bases will persist indefinitely. Badly, or unevenly pruned trees should be cut close with a power saw for a diamond trim.

Dates used in patterns of rows and curves have a tremendous grip on the adjacent space, and since full-grown trees can be planted in quantities for $60 to $70 a tree, shopping centers, new towns and golf courses are availing themselves of large numbers of them and should continue to do so in the desert areas.

Dates, although they will grow all right on the coast, often do not look very happy in a damp climate and refuse to fruit properly in the absence of scorching desert heat. In the luxurious foliage of the subtropics (Florida), or the cool tropics (Hawaii), they look quite alien and out of place and should not be planted. I wince every time I see the groups in Kapiolani Park in Honolulu consorting uncomfortably with monkey pods, shower trees and coconuts. And yet in the hot desert sun, whether near the Salton Sea or the Shatt-Al-Arab they look magnificent.

Beccari, the great Italian authority on palms, lumped this tall slender species from Senegal with *Phoenix spinosa*, a dwarf, many-stemmed species from South Africa. Horticulturally they hybridise so freely, especially with *P. dactylifera* and *R. canariensis*, that a vast and variable number of forms of this palm exist. All of them, fortunately, make excellent landscape subjects.

The Senegal date is one of the few palms (*Howeas* and *Archontophoenix* are others, but are not so hardy) which produces the desert island panache so beloved of ex-patriate Honolulu vacationers, trader's eating groups, and others who would like to turn southern California into a tropical paradise. The plant suckers freely, producing any number of relatively slender trunks rising from a common base. These support several heads of graceful, arching leaves. The fronds are bright, glistening green and are most elegant in the best trees. A Senegal date with six or seven good stems is one of the finest specimen plants in existence, and a patio or a swimming pool area dominated by such a group, if well designed architecturally, may need little else in the way of plant material.

By assiduously removing the suckers, thin, slightly leaning-trunked specimens may be created. This trunk may be only 4 to 6 inches thick. These single-stemmed specimens are beautiful trees, but in my opinion the clumping habit constitutes the chief charm of the species. So after reading the first sentence in this paragraph, do not react like one nurseryman I spoke to. "I quit growing it," he said, "I couldn't stop the darned thing from suckering!"

The foliage heads, the leaves, and the pinnae are less than one-half the size of the ordinary date palm or of the Canary Island type. The trunk is rough with old leaf bases which somehow manage to have a pleasant character. The flowers are not important in this species and the fruit, for a change, is not considered edible.

The Senegal date will grow a foot a year to start with, slowing down later and reaching perhaps 25 feet as a clump, 50 feet as a single tree. It thrives in rich, well-drained soil, using manure and fertilizer like the other palms. The tree is not so hardy as the large dates, and its hardiness probably varies a good deal with the individual plant, possibly because of the likelihood of hybrid blood. Small plants will often be badly burned and even defoliated by temperatures of 23° F. or 24° F.; temperatures of 18°F. or 20° F. may kill them, and will do so if there is any sap in the trunks. Large trees, however, probably due to hybrid vigour, have withstood temperatures of 20° F. without injury. There are instances where they have come through winters when the thermometer hit 15° F. (Indio). It would seem that hybrid seed from local sources should produce better and hardier trees than imported seed of the so-called true species, which growing in the tropics, as it does, is likely to prove tender. Obviously some good old *canariensis* or *dactylifera* blood will improve the situation.

Senegal dates can be grown on the coast and inland valleys from Santa Barbara south and in the desert, even in the colder areas, if they are protected as young plants during particularly severe winters. They are also much esteemed in Florida, and are grown in groups as dense screens in Hawaii.

Senegal dates provide some of the most versatile landscape subjects in existence. They are plants with a universal quality which makes them look good with most other plants or architectural features. They combine well with gingers, bamboos, tree ferns, elephant ears, and so on. They also look good with succulents and yuccas or with rounded forms like magnolias and gardenias. A small Senegal date will improve the texture of any paving or wall, and will naturally benefit from the protection these structures afford. Senegal dates look fine by the lake-

D.M.

shore and will stand sea spray. For this reason they might look much more pleasant on the coast at Santa Barbara, replacing the stiff formality of the robustas and Canary Island dates at present planted in rows along the seashore there.

The Senegal date is also an excellent street, or avenue tree, if reasonably large plants are used. In fact its only drawback is one of price: large full-grown clumps cost several thousand dollars; but smaller trees in cans or boxes cost only the same as other shrubs and trees of the same container size.

P. paludosa, a native of India, has been absorbed into the swarm of *reclinata* hybrids in the Southwest and landscape-wise can be considered the same species.

PHOENIX ROEBELENI [P. loureiri, P. humilis] *Dwarf Date Palm*

The Dwarf or Pygmy date palm is a very graceful, fine-leaved miniature palm growing to 8 feet eventually, but taking as much as 10 years to make a trunk. In the interim period it can be treated as a fern.

It is naturally suckering, forming several stems, but can also be easily trained to a single stem. The trunk is covered with persistent leaf bases and brown hair in a pleasant pattern. The leaves are up to 5 feet long, elegantly arched, soft and pliant, bearing 100 or more pinnae. The foliage is altogether plume-like, and in well-grown plants is almost breathtaking.

This is one palm about which much misinformation has been spread, largely due to its wide acceptance as a greenhouse and indoor plant. From my experience, this palm is extremely hardy, standing full desert sun and cold down to 18° F., when established. There are specimens growing in Phoenix in full sun and others throughout the coastal regions. In spite of this, it is native to subhumid Indo-China and should be used in shade with plenty of moisture for best results.

It is true that temperatures of 25° to 28° F. have been known to kill the dwarf date which has given it a wrongful reputation of tenderness. But this is undoubtedly due to greenhouse plants which have been planted out in the garden and have succumbed before they are acclimated in their new homes. If given shade and shelter, the dwarf date can withstand the worst the southern California coastal area can offer, in all areas where the smog is not too severe. It also grows well in the desert, in Florida, and in Hawaii. Flourishing in rich, moist soil, it will not tolerate bad drainage, and likes frequent summer watering.

The first small dwarf date brought to this country was sold for $500 and the plant was rare and expensive here for many years, according to Nehrling, because the monkeys ate the fruits and no seed could be collected. The demand was so great that a friend of Mr. Roebeling, the discoverer of the dwarf date, supplied him with guns to take back to Indo-China so that natives could keep the monkeys off the palms until the seeds were ripe for gathering.

P. roebeleni has numerous landscape uses when young (for the first 10 years.) It can be grown as a fern-like foreground for other trees and shrubs in protected places. It makes an excellent house or patio plant, and can be used for decorating dinner tables. Provided the soil is rich and well-drained, single or multi-stemmed forms will survive in pots or boxes of a foot or less in diameter. For permanent planting the dwarf date is good with a background of cycads, *Raphis, Chamaerops, Chamaedorea,* bamboo and tree ferns in innumerable permutations and combinations.

Native to the Sikkim Himalayas in India, the Cliff Date Palm in many ways resembles a stouter, shorter, single-stemmed Senegal date with a rather large, floppy, head. The leaves are long, and soft, almost limp, and quite unlike the stiffer leaves of the largest dates. The leaflets are arranged regularly along the midribs in vertical planes. This makes them flat appearing, so that sometimes only the edge of the leaf can be seen. They are fresh looking, green and striking, with an air of considerable refinement. The trunk is almost a foot in diameter, reaches 20 feet in height perhaps, and is covered with old leaf bases. The top of the trunk, in fact, can be quite heavy and unattractive if it is not pruned. After the leaf bases have abscissed or have been removed, the trunk is slightly ridged, but of even width, more in keeping with the crown. The fruits are small, borne in quite heavy clusters which are bright yellow and are very showy.

The hardiness range and soil requirements of the Cliff date palm seem to be about the same as those of the Senegal. It is a rare species, represented in collections like the Huntington Botanic Garden and Balboa Park, San Diego; and, although it is tender as a young plant, a few trees may be seen growing on streets in Phoenix, Arizona, where the temperature has been known to hit 16° F. It is also found in Florida.

Because of its small scale, it is a valuable addition for a wide range of landscape uses on small properties. It is also an excellent porch, patio, pot or tub plant in all stages of growth. Only the absence of this palm in the nurseries will prevent its widespread adoption as a fine tree for the southern California landscape and for the Southwestern desert.

THE LESS HARDY PALMS
These will stand 2 or 3 degrees of frost only. They are suitable for coastal regions.

ARCHONTOPHOENIX CUNNINGHAMIANA
Seaforthia Palm

This is the commonest of the less hardy palms on the Pacific Coast. The only other species often met with are the *Howeas*. The Seaforthia is easily distinguished from them by its shining green column of leaf bases, which sheath the top foot or two of the trunk, a property it shares with *Rophalostylis baueri*, a collector's item at the moment, and the tropical palms *Veitchia (Adonidia) merrilli, Dictyosperma alba* and others which are confined to Florida and Hawaii and similar tropical countries.

This is the palm called *Seaforthia elegans* in the trade and which is so widely grown as a conservatory and house plant throughout the world. Unfortunately, there has been a mixup in botanical nomenclature. The true *S. elegans,* now re-named in the inimitable way of botanists, *Ptychosperma elegans,* is a rather different palm, not unlike A. *cunninghamiana,* but smaller and less attractive, with 20 or more pairs of blunt leaflets on the leaves, whereas A. *cunninghamiana* has at least twice as many pointed ones and will reach better than 40 feet in height against *Ptychosperma's* 20. If you ask for S. *elegans,* a most euphonious name, you will get A. *cunninghamiana.* Since the true Seaforthia is not *Ptychosperma,* the name is going begging. So, seaforthia let it be! Surely it's less confusing that way.

The seaforthia is a most beautiful palm, with a tall, slender, prominently ringed trunk, topped by the bright green column of sheathing leaf bases. The splendid leaves which may be up to 10 feet long are flat in cross-section, unlike *Howeas,* and may be turned in a vertical plane, like the cliff date palm. The whole palm and its parts is completely smooth and spineless. The flowers are borne below the green columns on the trunk in a shower of amethyst, followed by masses of bright coral fruit, presenting a sight which is no less than stunning, with the elegant leaves and the gray trunk against a blue sky.

The seaforthia likes a rich moist soil, thriving on stable manure and fertilizer. It will take a lot of water when in growth and little when not. It is easily grown in pots from seed. Once established outside, seaforthias will grow rapidly at the rate of 2 or more feet per year. They seem to do their best near the sea coast, since in their native habitat of Queensland, Australia, they are found most abundantly at Cape York and Sunday Island. They are common in both Santa Barbara, where they are being planted as street trees, instead of the Queen palm, and in San Diego. They also do well in the coastal area in between these towns. Fine seaforthias exist inland, too, but protected localities are advised for the tree, since, although established specimens have been known to take 10° of frost, others and smaller plants have succumbed to 27° F.

There are several specimens in the open air at Los Angeles County arboretum, apparently thriving, and the palm has been grown under lath shelter as far north as Redding, California. It should have a wide range in protected patios, if not kept too dry, and grows exceedingly well in Florida and the tropics.

Archontophoenix alexandrae. The Alexander Palm is a similar palm with a swollen base to its trunk, grey undersides to its leaves (versus green in seaforthia) and leaves which do not fall below the horizontal. These palms together with *Ptychosperma,* and in the tropics, *Dictyosperma* and *Veitchia,* have similar values as landscape subjects. They look their best in groups with bamboo, *Strelitzia nicolai* and other foliage plants. They have the great advantage of dropping their own leaves cleanly without the aid of pruning.

A native of southern China in an area about 50 miles from the famous seaport of Canton, this fishtail palm shows evidence of being hardy in the coastal areas of California. A specimen has existed for 5 years in a not particularly protected location between two clumps of bamboo in the Los Angeles County Arboretum. It is now about 12 feet tall, has already endured 2 or 3° of frost, and is still in fine shape.

The fishtail palms have huge bi-pinnate leaves, bearing numerous triangular leaflets shaped like the dorsal fins of fishes. They are fully described in the tropical section of this book on page 78. Their chief characteristic, besides outstanding beauty, is their flowering. This process consists of huge hanging spikes borne progressively down the leaf axils of the trees, from top to bottom, normally with a male and female flower alternating down the trunk. The fruits which follow are attractive, but are highly astringent and will injure the mouth if eaten. However, since the tree takes many years to bloom and then dies, this is not a major problem.

If this palm proves hardy, its landscape uses are unlimited, since it resembles an enormous maidenhair fern and has a form and texture which will enliven any plant grouping or structural background. It's especially beautiful with golden bamboo, acanthus and Natal plum. It is not, however, a highly obtrusive form like, say, a Koster's blue spruce, or a New Zealand flax, both of which shriek for attention. In addition, the fishtails provide some of the finest tub and patio plants grown. Most of them like rich soil, plenty of water, and a moist climate, but I have a feeling this one will stand a wide range of conditions, including sun or shade. It should prove satisfactory on the coastal strip from Santa Barbara to Mexico and in protected corners and patios inland, especially on hill slopes where the air drainage is good. But in areas where there are consecutive years of freezing, these continued cold spells are likely to prove fatal as they did in A. Robertson Proschowsky's garden on the French Riviera.

P.M.

HOWEA FOSTERIANA   *Thatch Palm*

HOWEA BELMOREANA   *Belmore Palm*

These palms have a very narrow natural range, since they are native only to Lord Howe Island, a beautiful island in the Pacific. *Howeas* under their former name *Kentias* are grown throughout the world as pot plants, especially as rented plants for restaurants, and hotel lobbies; they are also used for weddings, funerals and all types of public and private festivities. Under such circumstances they endure the roughest kind of handling as well as drafts, chills, and changes of temperature. So much so that every few weeks they must be returned to a greenhouse to rest or they will die. They have to be tough to stand this sort of treatment and they are.

In cultivation *Howeas* hardly ever set seed, so the tremendous amounts required for the world's markets are collected by the natives on Lord Howe Island. This is the sole industry and the entire reason for the prosperity of the Island.

Howeas will grow under a far greater range than formerly suspected. Although they will stand frost down to 28° F. only, with any assurance, good specimens have been established at the Huntington Botanic Garden near Pasadena where they are under a large oak tree. Here with the help of an oil lamp they have withstood a temperature of 20° F. in the surrounding air for three nights running. On the coast from Santa Barbara to San Diego they are perfectly hardy and many fine specimens may be found. I have also seen them apparently thriving in full sun in quite windy gardens in San Francisco and the Bay region. I have seen others in full shade under a tree on the north side of a two story building in the grounds of the Desert Inn at Palm Springs. Walled gardens and patios are probably the best locations for *Howeas,* if good specimens are needed, with some protection from buildings or nearby trees. They are wonderful combined with all kinds of flowers or flowering shrubs like *Cassia alata, C. splendida,* camellias, *Raphiolepis* and begonias. They are also good with ground covers. The accompanying shrubs should always be rounded so as not to compete with the arching form of the *Howeas.*

Those who revere the south sea island approach should try large groups of *Howeas* with a bamboo fence, bananas, *Melianthus,* gingers and *Scheffltras* pruned as shrubs; and with cup of gold vines, giant bamboos, tree ferns and *Albizzia julibrissin* in the background. Black volcanic rock walls and flagstone paving will complete the picture.

Both species are tall, slender, feather palms with smooth trunks ringed by old leaf scars. The leaves are up to 10 feet long and are very graceful. There is no super-column as in *Archonthrophoenix.* The two species are easily differentiated, since in *H. fosteriana* the leaflets turn downwards and are softly drooping. The leaflets of *H. belmoreana* on the other hand turn upwards like a *Butia* and the fronds are strongly arching. The rare flower spikes and fruit are borne at the top of the trunk.

Howeas are slow to establish and need rich soil although they may eventually reach 30 to 60 feet. They are naturally upright but can be trained to any shape of form or mass. Under

good conditions *H. fosteriana* will grow 6 inches to a foot a year, *H. belmoreana* rather less than this. In southern California hundreds of thousands of *Howeas* are grown under lath every year for the eastern indoor market; more should be kept at home to help furnish our coastal gardens.

The Pondoland Palm is closely related to *Jubaea spectabalis* and to the coconut with a similar fruit which, although much smaller, contains milk. According to Robert Story a botanist in Cape Province, this handsome feather palm is found at the mouths of the Umsikaba and Umtentu Rivers in Pondoland, South Africa. Known locally as "Incomba", in spite of its restricted range the Pondoland Palm has been little disturbed, due perhaps to its proximity to a leper colony. Another deterrent to ardent collectors and plant hunters is the presence in the area of one of the world's most deadly snakes, the black mamba, which apparently likes the company of the palm.

David Barry, jr., of Los Angeles is responsible for the introduction of this palm into America, his seed source having beaten the boys, the baboons, the lepers, and the mambas in the seed collection stakes. This occurred in 1939, late enough that the palm is noted neither in "Hortus II" or Bailey's "Cyclopaedia of Horticulture." Mr. Barry found that a container at least 2 feet deep was necessary to stop the long hypocotyl from corkscrewing as it hit the bottom. In 1949, in the severe frost when the temperature dropped to 25° or 26° F. in his area of the coast, one-third of the 10 year old plants succumbed to cold, leading Mr. Barry to conclude they were about as hardy as *Howeas, Archonthophoenix* and *Rhophalostylis* (29° F.).

The plants split up naturally into several heads, the division occurring high in the crown of the plant and working downwards. Larger plants are easily divided by a saw. The leaves on Mr. Barry's plants are 6 to 8 feet long; but in Africa they may reach 15 feet. They resemble those of *Phoenix reclinata,* for which the palm was long mistaken in its native state.

In nature the palms may reach 20 feet in their very limited area. In the words of Mr. Storey ". . . a few [are found] on the outskirts of the riverine bush and the remainder on rocky shelving banks near the water, forming small thickets, sometimes stemless and at other times with stems about 6 feet high."

These palms must be hand pollenated but they have not set seed in any quantity in California yet. Effort should be made to increase the stock for use in groups in coastal gardens, and favored gardens inland, where this fine tree should combine exceedingly well with other foliage trees and shrubs.

RHOPHALOSTYLIS

A small genus native to New Zealand and Norfolk Island, comprising three species, two of which are grown ornamentally in the coastal regions of California and other warm temperate areas. They will stand very little frost, perhaps 2 or 3 degrees, although A. Robertson Proschowsky reports them hardy down to 23° F. on the French Riviera, and Commander Dorrien Smith says some old trees were not killed by 8 degrees of frost and 2 months of freezing weather in the Scilly Isles off Cornwall, England. As young plants they will stand no frost at all. They also need protection from too much hot sun and favor a moist climate.

RHOPHALOSTYLIS SAPIDA — *The Shaving Brush Palm*

In California the palm will reach 30 feet eventually, with a slender straight trunk (under 6 inches, usually), which has pronounced rings. At the top of the trunk is a prominent bulge, verifying the literal translation: "style like a club" of the generic name. About a dozen leaves up to 8 feet long project from this bulge on short stalks in a stiffly upright manner. The flowers are borne on a spadix at the bottom of the bulge like *Archon-*thophoenix species. They are pale purplish-pink in color and are followed by scarlet fruits which are quite striking.

The shaving brush palms make lovely and exotic groups, raising their heads from shrubby undergrowth as they do in their native New Zealand. They like it so well in Santa Barbara, they have naturalized themselves in some gardens there, under tall trees, in the company of *Seaforthias* (*Archonthophoenix*) and *Howeas*.

RHOPHALOSTYLIS BAUERI — *Norfolk Island Palm*

This fine palm is native to Norfolk Island where together with *Araucaria excelsa* it provides some of the most magnificent groups of plant sculpture in the subtropics. It is very popular as an ornamental in New Zealand. Resembling in many ways *R. sapida*, the Norfolk Island Palm has a heavier trunk and larger, more graceful leaves, similar to, but almost double the size of, *Archonthophoenix cunninghamiana*, the Seaforthia palm of the trade. These leaves are powerfully arched and are carved into numerous large segments.

In a protected coastal garden this palm should thrive from Santa Barbara to San Diego. According to David Barry, jr. of Los Angeles, who has grown palms for over 30 years, it is the finest single-trunked palm which can be grown on the Pacific coast of America. Few who have seen *R. Baueri* at its best will attempt to deny this claim. The following letter from him, published in *Principes,* the Journal of the Palm Society, may prove interesting.

"In the 1920's" Mr. Barry states, "*R. sapida* was in many yards in Santa Barbara. This species and *R. Baueri* were planted in rows under lath in Lejeune's Exotic Nursery in Santa Barbara. These plants were mature and fruited regularly. They were a source of seed for me at the time. I heard that the State Highway Department had bought this stock, but I have never seen the plants on any highway planting, so I assume that the stock has disappeared. As to the plants in the yards in Santa Barbara, Los Angeles money in the hands of specimen tree men long ago raided that city of fine plants. I have no idea where the palms went. However, if you had looked methodically up and down the streets of Santa Barbara I venture to say you would have found a few old plants in front yards.

"I recently bought from Bud Hallberg, the young man (at the Los Angeles State and County Arboretum) who cares for the palm section (with much pride) about two dozen seedlings of *R. sapida* that he had grown from seed taken off the ground below a mature parent that was in the park at San Diego. To sum up, there are probably a few plants of *R. sapida* around in the coastal belt of So. California, but hard to find. *R. baueri* has always been rarer. Too bad, as it is the finest solitary trunked palm that we can grow here. I am trying to get a lot of seed of it and its close relative, *R. cheesemanii*. The seed that they have been sending has been old. Since writing the above I showed your letter to Byron DuCharme who commented that Bud Hallberg said that there are some specimens of *R. sapida* at the Santa Barbara Mission and a number in the city of San Diego."

Rhophalostylis sapida.

TROPICAL PALMS

For south Florida and Hawaii.

Some make good tub or indoor plants in other regions.

CARYOTA URENS and CARYOTA MITIS

The Fishtail or Wine Palms

These palms which are closely related to *Caryota ochlandra* (see page 69) are less hardy. Although they will survive on the Pacific Coast and have been known to stand as much as 5 degrees of frost once established, they never look really happy outside a warm greenhouse in the winter. This is probably due to our 6 months season of cool and cold nights which is often more deleterious to tropical plants than actual frost. Anyone who has seen them in the tropics in all their splendor could hardly bear to see them suffering anywhere else. However, they make excellent tub plants for a sheltered corner or patio; and can be grown throughout the country if they are placed in a conservatory for the winter months. They grow well in southern Florida and in Hawaii. In their native haunts on the Malabar Coast in India these palms grow in groups in the moist tropical forests, and natives like to build their houses near them.

At first glance to me the leaves resemble those of an enlarged ginkgo, or maiden-hair fern. At a second glance, the huge cascading mass of fishes' tails and fins is apparent. The leaflets themselves are delta shaped and jagged at the end margins. The compound bi-pinnate leaves, which support the leaflets, may be as much as 20 feet long and 10 feet wide. They look like branches and are really magnificent plant structures.

C. urens may reach 80 feet in the tropics, perhaps half that height in Florida and Hawaii. Their trunks are smooth, slim, round, and quite straight. When the tree is mature it begins to flower, starting at the axil at the apex of the trunk and gradually working downwards.

Numerous flowers are borne on huge drooping spikes as much as 12 feet long, by 2 feet wide. When, after a couple of years, perhaps, the leaf axil at the bottom of the stem has produced a flower, the tree dies, but the seeds are so prodigally borne that, in its native state at least, it is soon replenished. The reddish, globular fruits contain a juice which is a skin-irritant from which *urens*, the specific name meaning "stinging," is derived.

CARYOTA MITIS

Dwarf Fish-tail Palm

A native of Burma and Malaya, *C. mitis* is smaller in all its parts than *C. urens*, reaching perhaps 20 feet ultimately and suckering to form a clump. Like its larger relative it will take light or shade, but needs protection from the hot sun as a young plant. This palm, too, is quite stunning in a tub. Both these palms are heavy feeders and drinkers, thriving in well-manured, rich soil.

Fishtail palms, especially *C. urens*, are economically of great value. String, ropes, baskets, and brooms are produced from their tough fibres. Toddy, or wine, comes from their sap. Old trees produce several gallons a day. An excellent sugar is also made from this sap and sago is extracted from the pith of the trees.

Ornamentally, the fishtails make excellent lawn specimens and fine groups, combining well with all types of bamboos and *Ficus* species. As I have already said, they are unusually fine plants in tubs which are effective in large homes, greenhouses, patios and similar places.

CHRYSALIDOCARPUS LUTESCENS

Yellow Bamboo Palm, Butterfly Palm
(Often called Areca)

A native of Madagascar like the traveler's tree and the royal poinciana, this palm was very popular as a house plant before the discovery of the *Howeas* (Kentias). It is a most beautiful plant with green and golden stems which are ringed like bamboo canes. The light green feathery leaves are elegantly arched. The leaf-

Chrysalidocarpus lutescens.

lets which are soft and very graceful, are turned in many directions, sometimes creating twisted effects and usually producing fabulous shadow patterns. The palm is suckering, forming a broad clump up to 20 feet high. Unless the young canes are pruned this clump will have some leaflets down to the ground, due to newer smaller canes being formed on the outskirts. If it is desired, these can be removed to show the bamboo-like structure more clearly, but it is doubtful if this constitutes an improvement.

The white fragrant flowers are in separate spikes borne amongst the leaves, and are succeeded by golden yellow fruits, from the seeds of which the new plants are easily grown. This bamboo palm will stand no frost but it thrives in South Florida and particularly in Hawaii where magnificent clumps are quite common. At different times a few plants have also been grown on the Pacific Coast, often

for several years in succession before they were killed by a frost. In spite of the long, comparatively cold winters the palm still looks chipper, unlike so many tropical palms in temperate climates.

The yellow bamboo palm makes an excellent pot or patio plant as long as it has rich soil and plenty of water. It also makes a wonderful specimen plant on a terrace or shaded lawn, since it needs protection from the hot midday sun.

This palm is excellent in practically any landscape situation as a group, a screen, a filler, or a background and combines well with low luxuriantly-leaved plants like spiderlilies, crinums, peperomias, crotons and ferns. Yellow bamboo palms are lovely beside water, with large well-placed rocks in the vicinity. They are also first rate foils for all types of structural or architectural elements in the vicinity. All-in-all they are as useful a landscape subject as can be found.

The coconut is probably the most widely useful plant in the world, as well as being one of the most beautiful. To the people who live within its range the coconut provides food, drink (milk and alcohol), sugar, medicine, clothing, thatch, logs, etc. All of this and beauty too—what more could one ask?

Almost wherever there are tropics you will find the coconut cultivated for some purpose or other. In fact some people consider that a true tropical climate is evidenced by the presence of this tree. Yet it is nowhere found in the wild state. Coconut seeds are viable even after weeks at sea and it is possible that seeds washed ashore on Pacific islands started the extensive groves found in these areas today. There is also a strong case for the coconut having traveled on the migrations of men, since few were likely to leave their source of livelihood behind when seeking homes in new lands.

Coconuts will grow right down to the beach. They will endure salt spray, winds, even brackish water and will apparently thrive on them. They will also grow well inland, standing great heat, but preferring small seasonal changes and a high rainfall. They reach their best development in really humid tropical climates with a mean annual temperature of 80° F. up, and a rainfall of 100 inches or over, such as those of Ceylon, the Philippines, and the islands of the south Pacific. In Hawaii they grow well, but do not bear as heavily as in the wetter warmer climates, and so they are not planted commercially. Coconuts will stand no frost and will not thrive in warm climates which have cool months. In Florida the coconut grows only in the extreme southern part, and there it is not economically important. They will not last more than a few years at a time in California.

The tree itself is a tall, slender, slow-growing palm reaching 100 feet in the same amount of years. The leaves are up to 18 feet in length, most graceful with numerous long broad drooping leaflets. The bole will twist and turn to reach the light so that a group of small coconuts can be very closely planted. They will soon establish visual equilibrium with each other, eventually making the finest grove of any palm.

The tree is easily started from the nut buried two-thirds in the ground, milk-end down; germination occurs in 6 months or less. These nuts will also sprout in water in the house much like a hyacinth or daffodil bulb. Coconuts thrown on the rubbish heap will usually make new plants. After about 6 years in their permanent location a fountain of gorgeous creamy flowers is produced, followed by the first nuts. An additional 10 years is usually necessary before the trees come into full bearing of 40 to 80 nuts per year.

Commercial orchards are planted at a distance of 30 by 30 feet or 25 by 25 feet. Copra, the dried white flesh of the coconut, is made into coconut oil and eventually into soaps and margerine.

Ornamentally coconuts can be planted in drifts or groves throughout a landscape to give it a background. Often little else but coconuts, sand, sea and grass is needed. It is yet another plant that has that universal quality which will combine with any other vegetation around. Large coconuts should be arranged to simulate the way the palms would reach for the light if they had grown there from the start. The group must be believable to feel right.

Any one who has experienced a nut hurtling past his head knows that larger coconuts have to be de-nutted annually. Consequently some people prefer the Samoan coconut which seldom exceeds 20 feet. Although all types will get by in any soil, coconuts grow best in deep rich loam.

*Coconuts at twilight
on the romantic island of Kauai, Hawaii.*

The double coconut, *Lodoicea mal-divica*, a native of the Seychelles, bears the largest seed known to man, which may take 10 years to ripen and may weigh 50 pounds. This seed was first found floating and was thought to be the fruit of some huge mysterious plant of the sea. It is a large, beautiful fan palm which grows only very slowly in Hawaii and takes 30 years to fruit even in its native haunts.

81

LATANIA LODDIGESII

PRITCHARDIA PACIFICA

Few forget their first view of this magnificent palm with its huge fans of brilliant silver in restless movement against a bright blue sky. Especially if it is a lone group on a grassy shore.

Like all *Latanias*, the leaf stem and leaf segments are edged with a vivid color, in this case scarlet-crimson. The leaves themselves are large, perhaps 5 feet in length, on long stiff petioles. They are sparingly borne, with an air of considerable élan on the stoutish grey trunk. The tree is slow growing; but may eventually reach 50 feet in Honolulu, where it is common, but not common enough, or 20 feet in the extreme south of Florida, where it is just hardy. It is also found, fortunately, in all moist tropic lands which are free from frost.

The Latan palms need rich well-drained soil; they do not care for sand or gravel. They also prefer a damp climate with lots of rainfall or irrigation water. The other species *L. commersoni* and *verschaffeltii* have purple and orange petiole margins, respectively, and are very striking, especially as young plants. All make first rate pot or patio plants when small. They also grow well in warm greenhouses or stove houses. They are native to Mauritius and the other Mascarene Islands in the Indian Ocean.

As can be imagined, any plants which have such a dominant form and color are not easy to use. Latanias are best by themselves on a large green lawn or in a good-sized terrace. Any other planting should be low and unobtrusive or of even texture, such as a background of rounded green-leaved trees. Ground covers should always be low and fine-leaved, or too much tension between them and the palms is generated. When properly arranged, a group of Blue Latans is one of the noblest sights of the tropics.

The Fiji Fan Palm was named after W. T. Pritchard, one-time British Consul in the Fiji Islands. Another tropical beauty which will tolerate no cold or frost, this palm is a fine landscape subject in most warm wet countries. Fiji Fans grow up to 30 feet tall, in a rather stiffly upright manner and are perhaps difficult to arrange; but the crowns have an unusual grace and the leaves are borne with the natural elegance of the aristocrat. Nehrling quotes Dr. Berthold Seaman, who first found this palm in the Fiji Islands in 1860. "[The seeds] germinate freely," he said, "and out of a handful thrown carelessly into a Wardian Case in Fiji, more than thirty had begun to grow by the time we reached New South Wales." He never found them truly wild, always in cultivation, with the best specimens perhaps 30 feet tall, "planted near the houses of the chiefs who regarded them as personal property." The chiefs also made their leaves into fans while their subjects had to make do with the less regal Pandanus for this purpose.

The crown is globular, supporting about 20 very regularly spaced light green leaves which are usually about 4 feet long and wide, with a maximum size of 6 feet. The leaves are soft with only small indentations and have a clean sculptural beauty. The flowers and purplish, cherry-like fruits are borne on spadices resembling curved drumsticks which present a powerful and unusual design together with the leaves. The trunk is slender, smooth, and grey and the total effect of the tree is that of a more refined tropical version of the Guadalupe palm.

The Fiji fan is just hardy in the extreme south of Florida where it needs protection from winds which injure its leaves. It grows well in similarly wind-free locations in Hawaii, in rich, moist soils and is found as an ornamental throughout the tropics of the world.

Fiji Fans, like *Latanias*, are not easy landscape material. They blend better with other plants than the latter palms because of their color, but their trunks tend to combine poorly in groups unless they are assembled with consid-

erable flair. The amateur should probably use them in groups of different sizes and allow them to grow upright. The artist can do wonderful things with larger specimens if they are available.

There are many other *Pritchardias* native to the South Pacific. Most of them in the hills of the Hawaiian Islands from whence at least one species, *P. beccariana* [see drawing facing page 1] has proved hardy and now grows in the open on the Pacific Coast. It has stood temperatures down to 29° F.

P. martii (Hawaii) and *P. thurstoni* (Fiji) are two other *Pritchardias* sometimes used in tropical landscapes. They are smaller in all their parts than *P. pacifica*.

If one were to chose a monarch of the vegetable kingdom, it would undoubtedly be the Royal Palm. Some plants, like some people, are so regal and so obviously well endowed with nature's gifts they completely dominate any landscape they inhabit. With a presence which commands attention and a nonpareil type of beauty, a mature avenue of Royal Palms is the most moving scene that can be organized by man. The Taj Mahal, St. Peter's, or Notre Dame are pale things by comparison. If a man wants to leave a mark on this earth greater than that of Michelangelo, Edward Stone, or Marilyn Monroe he should plant an avenue of Royal Palms.

There are fortunately several famous avenues already in existence. One of them is in the Peridiniya Botanic Gardens in Ceylon [see p. 113] where the trees are planted less than 10 yards apart, and are now 55 years old. Another is in the Botanic Garden at Rio de Janeiro where a large number of trees are now an average height of over 100 feet. They are topped by gracefully arched feathery fronds on a bole so smooth and perfect it could have been turned on a giant lathe by a master craftsman. These two avenues are of the Caribee or cabbage royal palms *R. oleraceae,* native to Caribee island, which may eventually reach 150 feet in height.

A smaller, rather less majestic Royal palm is native to Cuba where it is widely planted and where it has multiple uses for the natives. It is also well-known in Florida and in Hawaii, where it gows much less well than the Caribee Royal. According to W. H. Hodge in *Principes,* the Journal of the Palm Society, there is an excellent avenue of the Cuban Royal at the Lancetilla Experiment Station near Tela, Honduras. These palms are well over 50 feet tall. They are easily distinguished from the Caribee palms because of their elegant smooth white trunks which taper up and down from the larger middles. At the top of the palm is a green super-column of sheathing leaf bases from which the leaves strike out, and hang down. The leaves of the Caribee Royal are held, proudly, above the horizontal. They may be as much as 25 feet in length and 5 to 6 feet wide. The flowers are white, in trusses below the leaf-base column, and the fruits are borne in clusters of crimson berries.

A noble Royal palm is also native to south Florida where thousands were ruthlessly felled by realtors, "developers", and truck crop men until only two or three hammocks are left. But this is becoming the story of America. Fortunately a few trees are still standing. Some of them are over 100 feet tall.

Apart from avenues, Royals also make wonderful groups and masses preferably rising clear from the grass so that their structure can be enjoyed to the full. A background of trees, buildings, or a view throws their light trunks into sharper relief.

Royal palms will make rapid growth of up to 2 feet a year in rich, moist well-drained soil. They will take as much fertilizer and manure as you give them and are resistant to wind and sea spray.

GOTTSCHO-SCHLEISNER

Cuban Royal Palms in Florida. The agaves below compete with the palms, which should rise clear from a clean surface.

ARECA CATECHU

Betelnut Palm

A remarkably slender and erect palm reaching 100 feet occasionally, but, more often, half that height. The 8-inch trunk has bright green leaf scars on young trees, which eventually turn grey. The fan-shaped leaves are glossy green, with drooping leaflets above a green super-column of sheathing leaf bases. The lower leaves also tend to droop.

The betelnut palm is a beautiful and graceful tree when used in groups in any tropical landscape. It is native to Malaya and is widely cultivated in Asia, not for its beauty, but for its nuts which are yellow and the size and shape of a small hen's egg. In India, where betelnut production is a

$50 million industry, the pavements of many cities are plastered with huge red betel-juice stains emitted from the happy throats of betel-chomping Indians. The nut is chewed, together with lime, tobacco leaf, and a leaf of the betel vine. This act, although it lessens feelings of hunger in a land where such sensations are of prime importance, turns the teeth black and the saliva scarlet. It is reported to strengthen the gums and give the breath a sweet odour; but it does not improve either the appearance of Indians or of their paving.

The flowers of the betelnut are scented and perfume is made from them by the natives.

BORASSUS FLABELLIFER

Palmyra Palm

The Palmyra Palm is native to the desert regions of India, Burma, Malaya, and tropical Africa. It is a most valuable palm, completely supporting many people in the arid plains of southern India where it is hard to grow anything. It is estimated that over 100,-000 acres have been planted by the natives of that area and of Ceylon.

The Palmyra palm is so versatile that songs have been written about the 801 different services this tree renders to man. Old trees give excellent timber, the sap makes toddy or sugar, the leaves make fibres, mats, brushes, etc. The sap of the nuts is supposed to provide an unusually thirst-quenching drink.

The Palmyra has a tall trunk which may reach 80 feet in height and 3 feet in diameter, and is often, in younger trees at least, completely enclosed from top to bottom with a living cylinder

of rigid, green leaves. These may be 8 to 10 feet long, with a 4-foot spiny petiole. The female plants bear black fruits, half the size of coconuts.

The Palmyra is a comparatively fast-growing palm of noble size and proportions which is a valuable addition to the Hawaiian and other tropical landscapes. It will grow in the extreme south of Florida. It is excellent in avenues, groves, groups, or as a specimen where a rather large, striking plant is needed. In spite of its arid homestead it is reported, a Palmyra palm is growing in the greenhouse at Kew in the same humid conditions as the double coconut.

Palmyra palms are best planted in locations where they will remain permanently, as their hypocotyls go down three feet from the seed and are easily injured when the small plants are moved.

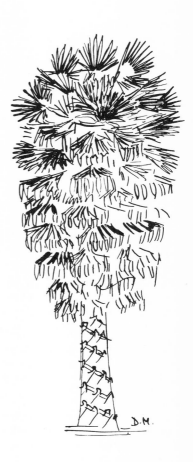

D.M.

CORYPHA UMBRACULIFERA (Left)   *Talipot Palm*

This huge palm is native to the moist regions of Ceylon and the Malabar Coast of India. The trunk, which is columnar and erect, will eventually reach 80 to 100 feet in height and 3 to 4 feet in diameter. It is surmounted by a crown of magnificent fan-shaped leaves which may be 12 to 18 feet cross, on stalks up to 15 feet in length. These leaves are one of the wonders of the plant kingdom.

Many people owe their livelihood to this palm and to its products. It is now grown in most of the tropical countries of the world. The leaves are used for large punkahs (fans), umbrellas, sunshades, and olas (whatever they are). The leaflets were once written on, and were the recipient of the sacred texts of Buddhist literature. The pith makes flour and the ivorine seeds are made into buttons and beads.

The flowering of the Talipot Palm is an awesome scene, which seems to personify the terrible brutality of primeval nature. When the tree is between 20 and 60 years old, yellow flowers are born in panicles up to 20 feet long. These are terminal from the bud, so that when flowering is over the tree must die. The effort of producing the flowers and fruits drains the leaves of all sap and kills them. Eventually, after a 2 year period, the leaves and fruits drop off, and only the stark, bare panicle is left, leaving the tree like a dead conifer in the landscape.

The Talipot Palm is probably better grown as an interesting specimen for its huge leaves than as an important feature of park or garden. Although very tender when young, established plants will stand up to 5 degrees of frost. This palm will grow in the extreme south of Florida and in Hawaii, but is quite slow and needs very rich moist soil and (in Florida at least) protection from harsh winds. It will also thrive in a tropical greenhouse.

ORBIGNYA COHUNE [Attalea cohune]   *Cohune Palm*

This gigantic palm is native to Mexico through Central America to Panama. It is massive in all its parts. The trunk, which is smooth and greyish, may reach 50 feet. It is surmounted by a crown of ascending, plume-like leaves as much as 30 or 40 feet in length — even the individual leaflets measure 3 feet or more. These leaves are particularly attractive in young plants. A heavy spadix of yellow flowers is followed by fruit clusters which resemble giant bunches of grapes. The individual fruits are like small ovoid coconuts, and yield an oil which is of better quality than coconut oil. This makes the Cohune important economically in those countries which are fortunate enough to coincide with the range of the palm.

Enormous groves are found in the Honduras where there are 15,000 square miles of Cohune ridges on rich fertile soils; these are interspersed with extensive drifts of sandy pine lands. The palms, which are regularly spaced at intervals of 50 feet, or there about, often look as if they were purposely planted. Occasionally they form magnificent natural avenues with their massive upswept fronds arching and meeting overhead, like the roof of a gothic cathedral.

Obviously this fine tropical palm should be used in groups in the landscape, or in avenues, rather than in single specimens which are inclined to look bizarre. In some areas the leaves brown badly and look ratty. The Cohune will grow about a foot a year in all tropical climates. Personally, I like to see the leaves pruned clean to the trunk, as the leaf stubs may look unsightly.

ACTINOPHLOEUS MCARTHURI (Above left) *McArthur Palm*

This native of New Guinea is a suckering cluster palm, much grown in Hawaii where the nuts seed themselves. The green ringed canes resemble bamboo and bear a profusion of dark feather-type leaves. The broad, blunt leaflets are cut obliquely at their tips "as if bitten off." The canes, which may reach 20 to 30 feet, are green when young and turn grey with age. The flowers are borne in grape-like clusters below the leaves and the fruits are a feature of the entire landscape in their season. Changing from their initial green through yellow to an eventual brilliant scarlet, they light up the country for miles around.

The McArthur palm is easily grown in the tropics in sun, or, better still, in partial shade. It is also a good greenhouse plant. Outside, use it in pots, patios or clumps as long as the area is free from wind. This palm is a good accent by the entrance path and makes fine groups with tropical shrubs and ground covers.

COCCOTHRINAX ARGENTATA (Above right) *Florida Silver Palm*

Another Florida native which also occurs in the Bahamas, this species will grow slowly to a height of 20 feet on a stem less than 6 inches in diameter. The leaves are round, small, and deeply divided, with silvery undersides. Unlike *Thrinax,* which has white fruits, those of *Coccothrinax* are black.

Silver palms make attractive small groups, if protected from the elements, since their leaves are easily torn by storms. They like a rich soil and are best in part shade. *C. argentea,* which is often confused with *C. argentata* is a native of Haiti, seldom found in cultivation.

COPERNICIA CERIFERA (Below left) *Brazilian Wax Palm*

This palm grows 30 to 40 feet high in its native Brazil where there are large forests of these trees. Their trunks, which are remarkably straight and slender, are covered with the prismatic projections of the old leaf stalks, arranged in spirals, and producing a marvelous textural effect in groups. The wood is very hard and has numerous uses. The handsome 3-feet-wide fan-shaped leaves are covered with wax, as are the fruits. The leaves are dried and the flaked wax peels off and is collected. It is of high quality, and is used for better-grade candles, phonograph records, furniture and floor polishes. Approximately two-thirds of a pound per tree per annum can be expected. The wax palm is the focus of an important economic industry in Brazil.

Groups of the wax palm can be grown in tropical countries for the rich texture of their trunks and for their columnar regularity. In rows they resemble the spiral pillars which support the arched roofs of Spanish patios. *C. australis* is taller and hardier and has been grown on the Pacific Coast.

CYRTOSTACHYS LAKKA (Below right) *Ceiling Wax Palm*

This very rare and extremely beautiful palm has numerous smooth slender canes like bamboo. These are up to 20 feet high, ringed and shining. The 3-feet-long feather-type leaves are of a glossy, dark green and clothe the entire plant. The chief characteristic of the palm, however, is the bright scarlet leaf stalk and its accompanying leaf sheath.

The ceiling wax palm is native to Malaya and, although not an easy subject, is one of the finest ornamental shrubs which can be grown. There are magnificent specimens in the Singapore Botanic Garden. With nearby water, soft green slopes, orange earth and a background of giant Saman trees, this palm is just terrific.

Mrs. A. C. Langlois, the well-known palmateer of Nassau, has found an excellent substitute, a *Mischophloeus* species, which has handsome leaves and orange-red leaf sheaths and which is apparently much easier to grow.

DICTYOSPERMA ALBA

Princess Palm (Areca)

This is a noble, proud, wild-looking palm which grows in dry, sunny places on Mauritius and the other Mascarene Islands in the Indian Ocean. It is found planted throughout the tropics and warm subtropics of the world, including southern Florida and Hawaii, where it thrives. The 8-to-12-feet leaves droop defiantly from the green super-column. The segments which may be 3 feet long and 3 inches wide, also tend to droop. The veins and petiole margins are red on young plants. The 30 feet by 8 inches erect trunk with its regular horizontal rings is flared at the base. Altogether, this palm has a distinct south sea island appearance.

The Princess palm makes a very good lawn specimen, growing fast in both sun and shade. It can also be used effectively in groups, groves or lines.

LICUALA GRANDIS

Licuala Palm

A most elegantly-leaved palm which is native to New Britain Island off Australia. The leaves are circular and folded like a pleated fan. The flowers occur in a free panicle, among the leaves, and are succeeded by scarlet bead-like fruits. The trunk is single, erect and 6 to 8 feet in height. A favorite stove house plant, *L. grandis* should be more widely planted outside in completely frost-free tropical areas. The plant will do well in south Florida, Hawaii, and the Caribbean; but it needs a shaded patio or protected spot where the easily injured leaves can display their full sculptural beauty.

THRINAX PARVIFLORA

Jamaica Thatch Palm

This native of southwestern Florida and the West Indies is a graceful, mop-headed fan palm which grows on a slender trunk reaching 30 feet in height and 6 inches in diameter. The leaves are most interesting. They are about 3 feet wide, deeply cleft, yellow-green above and silvery beneath. Although they grow on poor sandy sites in nature, *Thrinax* species prefer rich soil and full sun. These attractive little palms make excellent groups or specimens in those small gardens whose owners do not care to be smothered with tropical growth. They do well in Hawaii and are often used as pot plants in temperate climates.

VEITCHIA MERRILLI [Adonidia merrilli]

The Manila Palm

Superficially resembling the Betel palm, this native of the Philippines is a tropical palm which can be grown in south Florida, Hawaii and similar climates. It is a rather stocky tree with a straight or crooked trunk, reaching 10 inches in thickness and 20 feet in height. The leaves are strongly arched with vigorous upswept leaflets like *Howea belmoreana*. These leaflets are close together, broad at the middle and overlapping, giving the leaf a rather curious look.

This palm, which will stand no frost, grows well on limestone soils in Florida, and in Honolulu. As well as its attractive foliage, the Manila palm bears huge clusters of really gorgeous crimson fruits below the super-column which supports the leaves. The fruits are used occasionally as substitutes for those of the Betel palm.

The Manila palm makes good groves, groups, clumps, and specimens and is used in the same way as Seaforthias and other similar palms.

Manila, Princess, Licuala, *Jamaica Thatch Palm.*

NOTES ON PALM-LIKE PLANTS

ALOES (a)

These unusual plants bloom in February and March in the Southwest. *Aloe ferox* with bright crimson flowers, and *A. marlothii* with yellow and scarlet flowers, are two tree-like species resembling palms. Two hundred species of aloes grow in the south African deserts where they get little rainfall. Most Aloes, when established, will endure 10° or more of frost. They like full sun. They combine well with small palms like *Chamaerops* and desert plants like *Beaucarneas, Nolinas,* agaves, and yuccas. They are excellent, tough, pot plants, extremely easy to transplant and propagate.

BEAUCARNEA RECURVATA (b)

From the arid regions of Mexico, a most striking (and valuable) palm-like plant with a bulbous base. It stands full sun on the coast and inland valleys, but may need protection from the desert sun at noon. Once established, *B. recurvata* will tolerate considerable frost. Single trunked to 20 feet by nature at 20° F., or less, they will kill back and will come up again, multi-trunked. The leaves are ribbon-like and hang down in a light green mop, like the head of an English Sheepdog. *Beaucarneas* combine well with euphorbias, aloes, *Yucca gloriosa, Agave decipiens* and similar plants. They make really excellent specimens on terraces or patios.

CORDYLINES (DRACAENAS)

Native to New Zealand, Australia and East Asia, these rightly belong to the genus *Cordyline,* but they are known in most California nurseries as *Dracaenas.* They are small trees, with rather coarse, sometimes untidy, yucca-like heads. They make excellent tub plants when young and will usually grow indoors. They will not grow in the desert.

C. AUSTRALIS (c) (DRACAENA AUSTRALIS)

The common roadside tree of New Zealand is very hardy (to 10° F.), and will grow well in both dry and damp climates on the coast. This plant normally has a branched trunk to 25 feet, but it also makes a very interesting single-trunked tree. The leaves are narrow, and yucca-like. Many colored-leaved varieties are available.

C. INDIVISA (d) Huge leaves 6 feet long and up to 6 inches wide will stand only 4° or 5° of frost. *C. australis* is usually sold for this plant in California.

C. STRICTA (e) to 15 feet and normally wide spread. Likes shade and will grow indoors. Leaves up to 2 feet long.

C. TERMINALIS (f) "Ti-plant" of Hawaii. Branches, or sometimes single-stemmed, to 20 feet. Leaves 2 feet by 3 inches: used for hula skirts. Good thick screen in mass. Many varieties are available.

DRACAENA DRACO (g) *The Dragon Tree.* A native of the Canary Islands and a marvelous landscape subject with great character. Dichotomous, branching to 40 feet, with sculptural heads of regular, bunched, sword-shaped leaves. Young plants are hardy to 26° F. Old trees much hardier. This tree is good in groups, or as a specimen, but do not crowd it against a building.

94

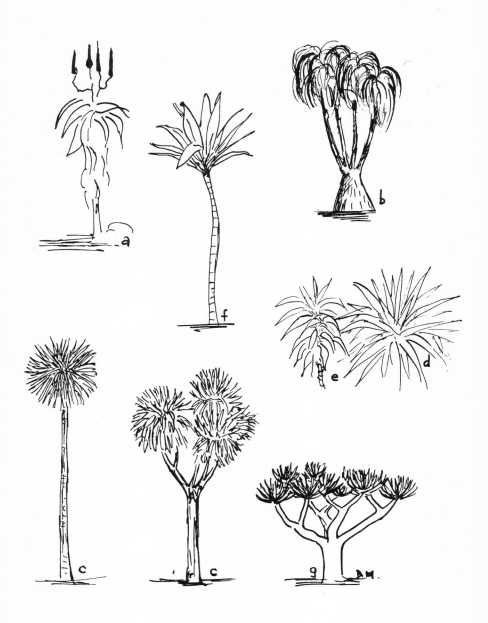

CYCADS

Sago Palms. More palm-like than the palms, they are actually primitive seed plants from the jungles of a former geological age. Cycads need a sheltered location, preferably part or full shade, near overhanging roofs, or small trees. They like a moist, rich soil and appreciate fertilizer and water when making new leaves in the spring. They also respond to a mulch of leaf mould, or decomposed peat, but they must have good drainage. All species combine well with tree ferns, bamboos and bamboo-like palms, such as *Raphis* and *Chamaedorea.* They are excellent for tubs, pots and planter boxes as arresting specimen plants. Even in open ground, containers will protect them from oakroot fungus, which can be a pest.

CYCAS REVOLUTUM (see photograph at City National Bank, Palm Springs, right). A very hardy plant, which endures temperatures down to 15° F. It is a native of Japan, where, since it is very slow growing, an old plant is a measure of family prestige. This cycad grows well on the coast from San Francisco south. It will stand full desert sun (Garden of Hotel Indio in Indio, and in Tucson), but prefers a moist, well-drained, shady location. Old trees branch and may reach 15 feet in a hundred years. Each branch holds 50 or more dark green fern-like leaves in heads like a miniature Canary Island Palm. Mature plants may be worth thousands of dollars.

DION EDULE (a) is hardy to 20° F. in southern California. It is native to Mexico. The foliage is aristocratic and most beautiful. Each stem has up to 40 superb leaves which are symmetrical with acute leaflets. It makes a good pot plant and prefers shade. The stem of *D. edule* will grow to 6 feet perhaps, but *D. spinulosum,* a related species, will reach 50 feet. This latter plant will stand no frost, however, and is usually a cool greenhouse subject in California.

ENCEPHALARTUS HORRIDUS var. GLAUCA (b) has blue spiny leaflets, giving it a very effective design value. A native of south Africa, it is hardy in southern California to 26° F.

MACROZAMIA DENISONI has fine foliage with very graceful, curving lower leaves. Grows in shaded positions on the coast and is also hardy to 26° F. Native to Australia.

ZAMIA FLORIDANA A U. S. native cycad which grows on the south Florida coast. Very small and too tender for California. Called the Coontie.

DORYANTHES PALMERI A native of the Australian desert is perhaps the most impressive yucca-like plant which can be grown in southern California. It has infinite possibilities as a structural design feature in the landscape. A full rosette of leaves may number 50 to 100. They may be 6 to 8 inches or more wide, and up to 8 feet long. There is an excellent specimen in the UCLA Botanic Garden.

MUSA, STRELITZIA, and RAVENELA

The bananas and their relatives are gross feeders and drinkers. They all need rich soil with a frequent manure mulch and lots of water. It takes a genius to fertilize them too heavily. Their leaves are easily torn by the wind, so they should be protected, preferably by the wall of a house or cabana, or by a high boundary fence. Or they should be planted in a warm sunny corner full of other foliage. They are good in groups with cannas, gingers, *Sabal minor, Rhapidophyllum hystrix,* etc.

MUSA ENSETE *The Abyssinian Banana* (below right). A single trunk to 20 feet, and 2 feet thick. The leaves are up to 15 feet by 3 feet. This plant takes several years to flower, then dies. The fruits are inedible.

MUSA CAVENDISHI *The Chinese Banana.* A dwarf species 4 to 6 feet high makes an attractive tub plant. Fruit is produced in warm climates.

MUSA PARADISIACA var. SAPIENTUM (below left). The common edible banana is many-stemmed, and each dies after fruiting or slight frost, and must be cut out. It is easily propagated by moving new offshoots. In hot or desert regions this plant is often used as a perennial. It will take up to 15° of frost, which kills the stems, but these come up again the following spring.

RAVENELA MADAGASCARENSIS (Photograph) *The Traveler's Tree* from Madagascar. Contrary to popular belief this is not a palm; but is a member of the banana family. The leaves are two-ranked in a single plane, like a huge fan. In the tropics it may reach 50 feet. It is called the Traveler's Tree, as it stores water at the base of the leaves near the stem. Unfortunately very tender, the Traveler's Tree makes an excellent background for other tropical plants in frost-free climates.

STRELITZIA NICOLAI *Giant Bird of Paradise* (Above right). Native to south Africa this *Strelitzia* is very much similar to the Traveler's tree, but is coarser, less regular, and it grows in clumps. It is hardy on the Pacific coast. *S. nicolai* stands 2 or 3 degrees of frost and will grow in protected locations (shade) in both Palm Springs and Phoenix. It is a handsome, if untidy, large-leaved plant to 25 feet, bearing blue and white bird-like flowers.

PANDANUS UTILIS (e)

Screw Pine. This plant is not hardy in California, although it might live a few years as a tub plant before succumbing to frost. The Screw pine is a marvelous specimen plant, with a powerful feeling of character. Up to 20 feet high, with a drooping head like *Yucca elephantipes,* it is supported by brace-like roots in triangular shapes. Pandanus makes excellent groups in south Florida and Hawaii on grassy shores with coconuts or *Pritchardias* behind.

D.M.

99

TREE FERNS

Superbly graceful, light green fronds arching from a trunk 3 to 20 feet high (up to 60 feet in nature) make the tree ferns first class landscape subjects. They are relatively easily grown from north of San Francisco (there is a large grove in Golden Gate Park) to the Mexican border. In their natural habitats on the Australian, Tasmanian and Hawaiian coasts, they are all similarly located with a high, light, forest cover. This is provided by eucalyptus in Australia and Tasmania and by Metrosideros in Hawaii. In all three locations they are on mountain slopes with good air drainage, and are subject to continuously moist off-sea winds depositing a high rainfall on the slopes, as the air is forced up the mountainside.

So give them shelter from wind, a rich soil and plenty of water. On the coast they will stand full sun, but they prefer partial shade. They will also take some frost, but they do not like it when young, so that a protected corner is advised. The soil should be one-third sandy loam, one-third peat, one-third good leaf mould. These ingredients must be well mixed. Tree ferns will stand organic fertilizer, but they are allergic to chemicals. Water from city mains may be too cold for their delicate foliage. Water which has been allowed to warm up to air temperature is therefore advised; an automatic atomizer is also an excellent idea.

At home on their moist mountain slopes, the trunks of tree ferns never dry out. The more moist they are kept in cultivation, as long as their roots are not soggy, the better and more luxurious they will grow. On dry days they should be liberally sprinkled *at least* once and preferably twice a day from overhead. Any sign of dryness in the fronds must be quickly remedied, as wilting means the loss of the leaf, and perhaps the whole plant. Tree ferns combine well with cycads and smaller ferns with oxalis, begonias or violas as ground cover. They are excellent in uneven-sized groups against a dark brown house or fence.

ALSOPHILA AUSTRALIS *Australian Tree Fern* (a). A hardy tree fern and one of the most beautiful, growing to 20 feet on the Pacific coast. It is a good tub plant.

Like *Dicksonia*, *Alsophila* is native to Tasmania and Australia. The leaves are horizontally held and are much divided, giving a lace-like effect.

CIBOTIUM CHAMISSOI *Hawaiian Tree Fern* (b). The leaves of this fern are less divided than the Australian tree fern, with more drooping fronds. It somehow manages to look Hawaiian. There were once over 600 square miles of this fern on the rain-lashed island of Hawaii, the largest of the Hawaiian chain, The Hawaiian tree fern is also known to grow in dry locations.

DICKSONIA ANTARTICA *Tasmanian Tree Fern* (c). This, the hardiest of all tree ferns, puts up with occasional frost and snow in nature. It is slower growing than the others, reaching perhaps 12 feet in cultivation on the coast. *Dicksonias* have small regular leaflets.

NOLINAS

NOLINA LONGIFOLIA *Bear Grass* (d). A plant closely related to *Beaucarnea,* and similar to this genus, with a fine shaggy head of very slender leaves. The flowers are yucca-like, borne from a branched stem of great character which may reach 10 feet. This plant is useful as an accent point, or as a group in desert landscaping. Bear grasses should be planted in 10 inches of decomposed granite, since they must have perfect drainage. They are native to Mexico.

N. PARRYI (N. BIGELOVII var. PARRYI) A Southwestern native, similar to the above, but growing to 6 feet only, unbranched, and not so graceful.

YUCCAS

The tree-like yuccas are often taken for palms, although they are more like *Cordylines* (Dracaenas) to which they are much superior. They are also much hardier, and will grow anywhere in the Southwest. Their foliage, too, is more positive in its design and cleaner cut. As a rule, they are slower growing than the *Cordylines*. Native to the U. S. and Mexico, they are of very simple culture, moving easily with rare losses — except in the desert, where they must be moved with great care, if taken from the wild, and must be given good drainage.

They have excellent structural value for all types of gardens as accent points, or in groups. They should not be used at the base of palms as they compete with the trunks, although a bold group with grass in between and palms behind is most effective. All yuccas have wonderful, creamy flowers fit for a king, borne in summer.

Y. ALOEIFOLIA (a, small plant). Tight rosettes of dark green aloe-like leaves to 25 feet. A beautiful young plant. Slow growing.

Y. AUSTRALIS To 40 feet with considerable trunk. The tree yucca common in the cactus garden at the Huntington Botanic Garden. Native to Mexico.

Y. BREVIFOLIA (b) *The Joshua Tree*, so called when the Mormons saw its wildly-waving arms they thought it was pointing to the promised land. Full-grown plants are available from cactus specialists in the Southwest. The Joshua tree must have good drainage in the garden. as it will perish under ordinary cultivation. A foot of decomposed granite is recommended. An unusual silvery grey-leaved tree to 50 feet. The silver leaves are striking against Palo verde blooms. There are huge stands of the Joshua tree in the Mohave desert and southeast of Kingman in Arizona.

Y. ELATA (c) Smaller version of Joshua, with beautiful fine-leaved symmetrical head. Native to the Southwest desert. Culture is as for Joshua. *Y. Elata* is reported to grow only 1 inch a year but large (old!) plants may be obtained from the wild (from private land, with permission, of course).

Y. GLORIOSA (d, young plant). A superb plant, hardy to 0° F. with a huge head of creamy flowers and magnificently carved dark-green foliage. Needs rich, fertile soil, as it is not a desert yucca. *Landscape architects and others should use this and other yuccas instead of the coarse, inelegant, and hopelessly over-planted* Phormium tenax, *the New Zealand Flax.*

Y. ELEPHANTIPES *Yucca gigantea* (e). A tree to 20 feet, with beautiful soft, wide leaves wnich may be 4 feet in length, and are most ornamental. This yucca has several luxurious heads, resembling a *Pandanus*. It needs protection from hot desert sun. and a rich fertile soil. There is a good specimen in Bullock's Shopping Center in Santa Ana, California. Will frost burn at 22° F.

Y. RECURVIFOLIA [*Y. pendula*] (f). Branched to 6 feet. Probably the most useful yucca. Hardy to 0° F., with good clean foliage and fine flowers. Makes excellent groups with blue and variegated agaves, or among fine-foliaged perennials and shrubs. This plant will take any range of garden conditions, since it is another moist climate yucca, native to Florida.

Y. WHIPPLEI (shown in the photograph) is native to the Arizona and California deserts where old plants bloom once, but gloriously, and then die.

EXTRA LIST OF PALMS

Notes on some palm genera and species whose names you may come across in your reading: some of these from the point of view of the landscape architect are inferior landscape subjects to those which have had lengthier treatment on the preceding pages of the book. Many, however, are exceedingly handsome tropical rainforest palms used in hot tropical climates, stove houses or warm greenhouses, all of which are outside the scope of this book.

Figures in parentheses indicate killing frosts in Proschowsky's garden on the French Riviera.

ACANTHOPHOENIX CRINATA AND A. RUBRA Mascarene Islands. Two species of elegant long-leaved feather palms for moist tropics or greenhouses, with slender spiny trunks to 60 feet. Fronds droop like *Howea fosteriana.* (37.4° F.)

ACANTHORIZA ACULEATA Mexico. Spiny trunked fan palms to 40 feet. Completely divided leaves droop irregularly at ends of long petioles giving tree bizarre prehistoric appearance. (32° F.)

ACELORRAPHE - PAUROTIS

ACROCOMIA *Gru-grus* America. Stately feather palms like Royals only with numerous black spines on trunks which may be dangerous to children. Of 30 species, A. *totai* most common, reported hardy to low 20's, has stood 18° F.

AIPHENES CARYOTAEFOLIA S. America. Slender tree to 30 feet in S. Florida. Handsome acanthus or ruffle-like foliage unusual for a palm. Trunk and leaves covered with spines.

ARECA TRIANDRA and about 15 other species in S. E. Asia and Australia. This beautiful palm has green ringed stems to 10 feet, making an excellent landscape specimen in shaded locations. (27° F.)

ARENGA ENGLERIA Very hardy (to 15° F.) bush feather palm to 12 feet across. Good tub, pot, or patio plant. Full sun on coast but better in shade.

ARENGA PINNATA and several other species of sugar palms in India and the E. Asian tropics produce sugar from sap collected from flower stalk. Huge erect, shaggy leaves. Economically important palm.

ARIKURYROBA SCHIZOPHYLLA Brazil. Small rather odd single-stemmed feather palm, which is grown outside in Florida.

ASTROCARYUM Mexico to Brazil. 30-40 species of erect feather palms with very spiny leaf stalks. Tropics and warm greenhouses. (32° F.)

BACTRIS *Gris-gris* Tropical America. Perhaps 200 species of small cluster feather palms, mostly spiny. Occasionally grown in greenhouses and outside in warm tropics. Many species very handsome. (32° F.)

BACULARIA Queensland, Australia. Three species, small slender feather palms. Related to *Areca* and *Kentia* and often confused with them by both botanists and laymen.

BALAKA SEEMANI Fiji. Single, straight, bamboo-like stems. Tops like *Ptychosperma* only more attractive. In fact a most graceful palm.

BENTINCKIA Tropical India. Two species of tall slender feather palms to 70 feet. Elegant, halfway between princess palms and coconuts.

BISMARCKIA NOBILIS Madagascar. Large magnificent fan palm to 200 feet. Grown in S. Florida, warm greenhouse, and tropics.

BRAHEA DULCIS and B. CALCAREA Mexican fan palms hardy on the Pacific Coast. B. *dulcis* grows in clusters to 20 feet. (20° F.)

CALAMUS West Africa, China, India, Malaya, etc. Over 300 species of climbing spiny palms used for rattan furniture. Tropics and greenhouse. Stems to 500 feet and 3 inches thick. (38° F.)

CALYPTROCALYX New Guinea, Tropical Australia. Five species, attractive feather palms with flat well-shaped leaves. Conspicuous red fruits on 10 foot spadices. (32° F.)

CALYPTRONOMA Cuba, Jamaica, etc., and South America. Ten species Large feather palms like Royals.

CATOBLASTUS Mountains of Colombia and Venezuela. About six species, black-barked cluster fan palms to 50 feet. Roots are like stilts above ground.

CEROXYLON ANDICLUM Famous wax palm of Andes of Colombia and Venezuela. Huge feather-type leaves. Wax on trunk. Used in tropics and fine warm greenhouse palm. Twenty other species.

CHAMAEDOREA One hundred species, graceful tropical American feather palms. Many are hardy to 25° F. Most are good for greenhouse, pot and shady patio.

CLINOSTIGMA Three species, Lord Howe Island, Samoa, Fiji. *C. mooreanum* dwarf, attractive Howea-like feather palm with purple ringed stem to 8 feet. (Reported to be hardy.)

COELOCOCCUS Six species, Polynesia, with drooping leaflets. *C. amicarum* feather palm to 50 feet with drooping leaflets. Ivorine seeds used for buttons.

COLPOTHRINAX WRIGHTII Cuba. Bulge-trunked bottle palm. Most unusual trunk like snake which has swallowed sheep. To 40 feet.

COPERNICIA Caribbean and South America. Thirty species. Hard wooded, wax palms. Beautiful, regular fan-shaped fronds. *C. australis* hardy at Riverside, California.

COROZO OLEIFERA South and Central America. Feather-type oil palm related to African oil palm. Trunk prostrate.

CRYOSOPHLIA *(Acanthorrhiza)* Mexico and Central America. Five species of tall, thorny-trunked fan palms.

CYPHOKENTIA New Caledonia. Three species, small feather palms like *Kentias.* (27° F.)

DAEMONOROPS Southeast Asia. Ninety species tropical, climbing, feather rattan palms. (32° F.)

DECKENIA NOBILIS Seychelles. Handsome slender feather palm like *Aconthophoenix,* but growing to 150 feet. Like other Seychelles palms not easy to grow in cultivation.

DESMONCUS Tropical America. Fifty species of spiny climbing feather palms. American equivalent of Asiatic rattans.

DIDYMOSPERMA India and Malaya. Eight species, very small warm house or tropical feather palms. Attractive leaflets often like *Caryotas.* (25° F.)

DIPLOTHEMIUM Brazil and Paraguay. Six species, handsome dwarf feather palms. Tropics or warm greenhouse.

DRYMOPHLOEUS Moluccas, New Guinea. Twelve species of handsome feather palms with smooth, ringed trunks. Related to *Ptychosperma.*

DYPSIS Madagascar. Twelve species, usually dwarf cluster-forming bamboo-like palms closely related to *Chamaedorea,* but not often as attractive. Tropics and warm greenhouse. (38° F.)

ELAEIS GUINEENSIS and seven other species. West African oil palms, producing high grade oil for soap and candles. Feather palm to 30 feet. Grown in Florida. (32° F.)

ELEUTHEROPETALUM Mexico. Two species, dwarf feather rain-forest palms like *Chamaedorea.*

EREMOSPATHA Africa. Twelve species. African equivalents of climbing rattans. Spiny trunks to 100 feet. Tropical and greenhouse. (38° F.)

EUGEISSONA Malaysia. Six species. Almost stemless large feather palms. Handsome erect leaves to 20 feet. (34° F.)

EUTERPE EDULIS and 50 other species. West Indies, Central and South America. Usually tall slender feather palms with elegantly articulated heads. Stem tops widely used as cabbages. Fruits also eaten. (30° F.)

GAUSSIA Slender attractive pinnate palms to 100 feet. Two species grown in Florida. Native to Cuba and Puerto Rico where they grow on poor rocky sites on sides of limestone mountains. Resemble Royals.

GEONOMA Tropical America. Two hundred species, dwarf palms with feathery-type fronds often with segments joined, forming huge banana-like leaves with a large V-shaped terminal cut as in *G. decurrens*. Most effective in the landscape.

GUILIELMA Costa Rica to Brazil. Seven species. *G. gasipaes,* Peach palm. Tall cluster palms with many heavy (6 inches) ringed trunks to 60 feet and feathery heads like small Queen palms. A magnificent tropical palm.

HEDYSCEPE CANTERBURYANA A single handsome feather species like a *Howea* and native to Lord Howe Island. Usually called *Kentia* or *Veitchia.* Common as pot plant. (30° F.)

HEMITHRINAX Cuba. Several species like Thrinax to 40 feet. Little known. Compact fan heads.

HETEROSPATHE ELATA Indonesia to Philippines. Handsome tropical feather palm with smooth ringed trunk. Grown in Florida.

HYDRIASTELE Several species like *Ptychosperma.* Tropical tub and greenhouse plants.

HYOPHORBE INDICA and H. VAUGHANII Mascarene Islands. Other species now referred to *Mascarena.* Very rare, pinnate palms not particularly ornamental. (36° F.)

HYOSPATHE S.A. A dozen attractive species like *Chamaedorea.*

HYPHAENE INDICA and THEBAICA *Dhoum or Gingerbread Palms.* Thirty or more species. India, Africa, Arabia. Handsome slender-branched fan palms to 40 feet. Grown in South Florida and Hawaii. Do not transplant well. Only branched palms in existence.

IGUANURA Malaya. Several species dwarf cluster palms with pinnate or joined leaves.

IRIARTEA CORNETO South America. Stilt palms. Supported by tall stilt-like roots as *Pandanus.* Handsome feather palms to 40 feet.

IRIARTELLA Several species, South American tropics. Small slender pinnate stilt palms.

JESSENIA Five species in West Indies and tropical America. Large attractive ascending feather leaves. Slender trunk to 50 feet.

KENTIA Most Kentias offered by trade are *Howeas, Hedyscepe, Kentiopsis,* etc. Seven true species, north Australia and nearby Islands. Resemble *Howeas.* Botanists' delight.

KENTIOPSIS Three Australian species. Like *Kentias.* More botanists' delight. (Also like *Hydriastele* and *Drymophloeus* which are like *Hedyscepe.* See above.)

KORTHALSIA Thirty species of spiny climbing rattans from India and Malaysia. Attractive pinnate foliage.

LEOPOLDINIA Brazil. Medium-sized feather palms. Trunks have fibrous net-like coverings, usually in upper reaches.

LEPIDOCARYUM Tropical South America. Several species. Rare delicate dwarf fan palms growing on forest floor in complete shade.

LINOMA Synonym for *Dictyosperma.*

LINOSPADIX Ten species, rare dwarf tropical feather palms from New Guinea. Bright bronze new fronds.

LODOICEA MALDIVICA Double coconut from Seychelles. Extremely handsome full-foliaged tree. Nuts may weigh 50 pounds.

LOXOCOCCUS RUPICOLA Ceylon. Hillsides and poor exposed rocky sites. Feather cluster palm to 20 feet.

MALORTIEA Very dwarf (2 feet), Central American palms like *Reinhardtias.* Warm greenhouse or stove house.

MANICARIA A few species. Medium-sized palms. Central America. Enormous (to 30 feet) Geonoma-like leaves. Will grow in swamps.

MASCARENA LAGENICAULIS and VERSHAFFELTII Mascarene Islands. Oddly attractive feather palms which grow in south Florida with bottleshaped trunks and beautiful curved foliage.

MAURITIA Amazon. Fifteen species. Tall, most interesting tropical trees with long leafstalks and fine foliage. To 150 feet. Make wonderful groups in tropics. Leaves fan-shaped. (26°-32° F.)

MAXIMILIANA Trinidad and Brazil. Tall, interesting feather palms resembling Cohunes. Several species.

METROXYLON *Sago Palms.* A dozen species in Malaysia and Polynesia. Sago of commerce is extracted from trunks. Trees flower and then die in manner of *Corypha.* Handsome, cluster feather palms, to 40 feet, requiring water at the roots. (41° F.)

MISCHOPHLOEUS Celebes. Fine cluster palms with conspicuous orange-red leaf sheaths. Good substitutes for Ceiling Wax palm. Prefer shade.

MORENIA Attractive feather palms to 30 feet. Resembling *Chamaedorea.*

NANNORHOPS RITCHIEANA North India. Afghanistan. Small, rare, bushy feather palm which tolerates snow and ice in native hills. An arid desert species known to have withstood 14° F.

NENGA WENDLANDIANA Indonesia. Small feather palm like *Howeas* and *Hedyscepes.* Prized by botanists (see *Kentiopsis*). (32° F.)

NEPHROSPERMA Tropical feather palm from Seychelles Islands, to 40 feet. (38° F.)

NIPA FRUTICANS *Nipa Palm* of the swamps and seacoasts from tropical Asia to Australia. Likes brackish tide-water where it forms an interesting but impenetrable mass of feathery fronds. Good for waterside.

NORMANBYA NORMANBYI *Australian Black Palm.* (The botanist who named it stuttered). Gorgeous slender tropical feather palm to 60 feet with dark trunk. Makes good groups. (32° F.)

OENOCARPUS Perhaps 20 species of fine tropical, bamboo-like clustered feather palms. Native in the Canal Zone. *Oe. panamanus* to 70 feet is common in Central and South America. (32° F.)

ONCOSPERMA Half a dozen species in Malaysia. A really magnificent cluster feather palm which makes a superb landscape subject in the moist tropics. Trunks bamboo-like, often spined. To 80 feet. (36° F.)

OPSIANDRA MAYA Guatemala. First found growing round ancient Mayan ruins. Fine, slender, single-trunked feather palm to 60 feet. Trunk prominently ringed. Leaves upswept.

ORANIA A few species in Malaya and the Philippines, of rare but magnificent feather palms, 30 to 40 feet high with slender trunks and long drooping leaflets like *Howea fosteriana.* (32° F.)

PARAJUBAEA COCOIDES Ecuador. Tall growing feather palm with fine round head. Hardy to at least 25° F. Up to 9,000 feet in the Andes.

PAUROTIS WRIGHTII Florida, West Indies. Cluster-forming fan palm with small heads. Hardy to 20° F. Interesting landscape specimen in Florida, but slow growing on Pacific Coast.

PELAGODOXA HENRYANA Central America. A beautiful small tropical palm with paddle shaped leaves.

PHOLIDOCARPUS Malaya. Rare fan palms to 80 feet, like Livistonas. Will grow in wet or swamp-like areas.

PHYTELEPHAS Tropical America. Twelve species. *P. macrocarpa* handsome feather palm. Short trunk. Twenty foot leaves with 25-pound fruit containing ivory-like nuts, worked like ivory. (32° F.)

PIGAFETTIA Malaya and Indonesia. Five species. Rare, erect palms to over 100 feet, rising from tropical island jungles. Hard to grow except in acid soils with high rainfall, but most beautiful with dark green trunks which have shiny joints.

PINANGA Fifty species. India to Indonesia. Leaves of a forceful elegance. Pinnate or entire usually on many slender stems in tight clumps. Handsome landscape subject, usually in shade. Six to 30 feet. (41° F.)

PLECTOCOMIA More East Asian climbing rattans which have leaves up to 30 feet and die when they fruit. Several species.

PLECTOCOMIOPSIS More Malaysian rattans similar to *Plectocomia,* differing only botanically.

PODOCOCCUS Two species of small slender feather palms from tropical Africa with interesting wedge-shaped leaflets.

POLYANDROCOCCUS Brazil. Small feather-palm with large 15-foot leaves and smooth trunk to 20 feet. Brilliant orange fruit. Like *Diplothemium*.

PRESTOEA A few species of small tropical feather palms from West Indies and Central America allied to *Euterpe*.

PSEUDOPHOENIX SARGENTII Native to Florida Keys. Has orange fruit like a cherry. Small spindle trunk to 20 feet, curved feather leaves. Interesting only as young plant or curiosity. (28° F.)

PTYCHORAPHIS Malaya to Philippines. Several species of attractive tropical palms with solitary or clustered stems and feather leaves.

PTYCHOSPERMA Queensland. Another genus which has been hopelessly confused in nomenclature (see page 68). *P. elegans* a handsome palm resembling *Arcontophoenix,* but with a slightly wild and odd appearance. (32° F.)

RAPHIA 20 species. Tropical Africa. One species tropical America. Stout-trunked with huge feather foliage. Tremendous leaves to 50 feet. Source of raffia.

REINHARDTIA Mexico. Central and South America. Five species, small graceful feather palms grown in greenhouses. Like *Malortieas* (if you know what I mean). (38° F.)

RHOPALOBLASTE A few species. Small, Indonesian tropical feather palms like *Ptychoraphis*.

RHYTICOCOS AMARA West Indian feather palm to 80 feet. Tall, slender, like coconut.

ROSCHERIA MELANOCHAETES Stunning feather palm from Seychelles, with slender ringed trunk, short, arching fronds and broad, pointed, widely spaced leaflets.

SCHEELIA Forty species from Mexico to Paraguay. Pinnate palms with erect fronds like *Orbignya cohune.* Rare in cultivation.

SERENOA REPENS The native saw palmetto of Florida, found in large colonies of fan-filled, bushy masses. Hardy to 12° F. Good in pots. or, as unusual ground cover, in gardens of both coasts.

SIPHOKENTIA BEGUINEI Malaya. Small fan palm with leaves of a startling beauty. Prefers protection from hot afternoon sun.

SOCRATEA Several species of South American stilt palms like *Iriartea.* To 80 feet with 10-foot stilts.

STEVENSONIA BORSIGIANA Another beautiful tropical palm from the Seychelles with orange underleaves, which are ellipsoidal and only slightly cut. To 50 feet, but an excellent specimen as a young plant.

SYAGRUS Fifty species of S. American feather palms. Landscapewise like small Queen palms. *S. macrocarpa* has withstood 20° F. on the coast. *S. weddelliana* is a dwarf palm, widely grown as a house plant under the name *Cocos weddelliana.* It resembles a more erect form of *Phoenix roebelinii.*

SYNECHANTHUS Small Central American rain forest palms like *Chamaedorea.*

TEYSMANIA ALTIFRONS Rare Malayan palms related to *Licuala* with short trunks and large entire leaves like canoe paddles. Warm greenhouse or tropics.

VERSHAFFELTIA SPLENDIDA Another handsome species from Seychelles with large leaves and stilt roots. Slender trunk to 80 feet.

WALLICHIA Himalayan feather palm with a few short cluster trunks and large upswept handsome leaves.

WELFIA Rare tall feather palms from Central America.

WETTINIA More South American stilt palms.

YUBA *Yu-yu Palms.* About 20 species of small Bactris-like feather palms from South America.

ZALACCA A dozen interesting species from East Asia. Stove house and stemless, often spiny and swamp-loving like Nipas.

ZOMBIA Small, cluster fan palm from Haiti.

PALMS IN THE LANDSCAPE

An avenue of date palms on the skyline leads to the farmhouse. A field of corn combined with the palms produce a landscape of noble scale.

Before attempting to arrange palms in the landscape a little study of the noble profession of landscape architecture will be most valuable.

It has often and rightly been pointed out that landscape design is an art and must be approached as an art. What is usually overlooked is that landscape design is the greatest of all arts, the only one with time on its side as a factor in the design process, and an art that denotes the full flowering of a rising culture.

During the 17th century, Francis Bacon in his essay "On Gardens" wrote "that when ages come to civility and elegancy, men come to build stately sooner than to garden finely; as if gardening were the greater perfection."

All the present day signs point to a new Golden Age in landscape architecture.

Until about 20 years ago, there were only two styles of landscape design in vogue in America. These were the formal style (page 115) which was derived from the axial symmetry of the great French and Italian gardens; and the naturalistic style which stemmed from the easy flowing contours of the English landscape gardens.

Many fine examples of both these styles exist in this country, but the limiting of a design approach by repeating elements mirror-like on either side of an axis; or, alternatively, the elimination of all manmade structures, has now been discarded. It has been

Palms are unequalled as impressive borders for avenues, streets or paths.
This double row of Washingtonia robusta *is by far the finest architecture*
on the campus of Arizona State University.

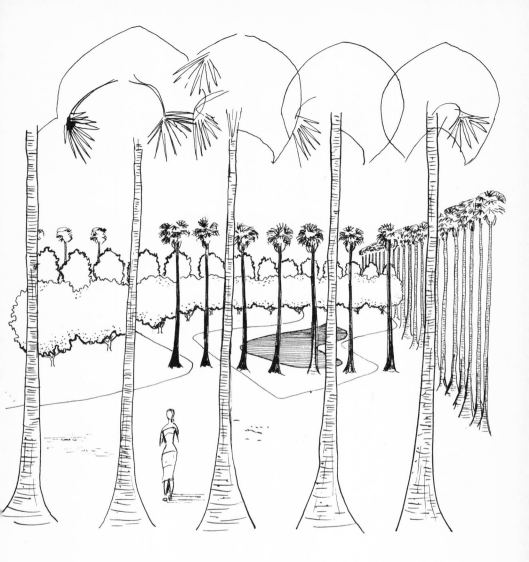

Palms can be used as space dividers giving form to large volumes of air.

found that asymmetrical arrangements of formal gardens are possible; at the same time there is no reason why structures cannot be combined successfully with informal plant groupings.

Today there is complete freedom in design. Abstract pattern usually provides the skeleton of the garden, with trees and shrubs the flesh and clothing. The placement of plant material is therefore often final and is of great importance to the design. The drawing on page 111 indicates the release from tradition which the contemporary trend has given to the arrangement of palms.

In the meantime, so-called naturalistic design has too often been replaced by the static dullness of the gardenesque - patio - informal arrangement so commonly displayed in magazines. Or by no design at all, which is sometimes preferable.

Whether used in the mass (in subdivisions, for instance) or as individual specimens in home gardens, the careful arrangement of palms is one method by which form and coherence can be returned to landscapes.

The landscape designer, whether professional or amateur, when using palms on any scale at all is taking on an enormous responsibility, for he can make or ruin the landscape for miles around. He must first throw aside all dogmas and preconceived notions. Here is no place for the faint hearted, he must be wildly keen.' He must project himself into the future landscape so that every molecule of form and texture present and future is registered on his design antennae.

The final result should have a feeling of rightness, fitness and inevitability. He should not aim for something cute or nice, he should aim for the sky. He is arranging some of the finest scultpures known to man, which are superbly articulated, perfectly unified . . . plant sculptures whose fundamental relationships of leaflet to frond, of blade to rachis and of the whole foliage head to the towering stem is already a work of art with which man cannot compete. And the palm tree is alive.

The design process involves organizing the landscape, whether countryside or city, school or campus, road or river, into a number of separate space cells unified in themselves and co-ordinated indivisibly with the greater landscape. The spaces, large and small, must be moulded by the structural use of palms in combination with other plant forms, paving, lawns, water, and buildings so that every glistening frond and textured trunk, together with every brick and blade of grass, has a concentrated and cumulative impact on everybody who finds himself in that particular area.

An awareness of these forms and colours is subtly brought to the onlooker, so that he is charmed, fascinated, entranced, stimulated, thrilled, and, above all, satisfied. Perhaps he should be a little awed with the strangeness of something which can bring so much content.

Now, in a democracy such as the one we live in, this is not easy to do an any size or scale. But it is possible. In Scandinavia design is an integral part of the way of life, so that legal controls and sensitive hands make all landscapes beautiful. In the new capitol city of Brazil — Brazilia — talent, money and legal power are making a great landscape with buildings a reality. But in our society the gimlet-eyed realtors and bankers seldom allow architects more than a few acres for a unified production. So we must turn to palms and to all vegetation until we get the laws, the educated public, and the deep-seated desire for better things.

A certain amount of experimenting may be all right to get the relaxed, if, often, chance, effects of much of our home planting. With larger landscapes, plants so permanent and so dominating as palms should be arranged only by the most able and practical landscape architects available; for only the landscape architect has the background and training to consider the more intimately aesthetic and esoteric uses of palms.

The illustrations have been chosen in the main from actual designs we have done, so that palms are shown as elements of the design process, rather than the reverse and more doubtful idea of designing with palms. Most landscape architects would consider them as forms in an organized design. For the sake of this book, however, they may be subdivided into towns and groves, fields and lines, groups and individual specimens.

The famous avenue of Caribee Royal palms at the Peridiniya Botanic Gardens, Ceylon.

D.M

Dates and citrus in formal rows bring satisfying unity to this subdivision. Although this is a former orchard, the same effect is possible from planning. The houses in this instance are completely subjugated to the planting.

Palms in a more "naturalistic" setting in the Fairchild Tropical Garden, Coconut Grove, Florida. A brave attempt to bring order into a garden designed mainly to show off the different species. W. L. Philips was the landscape architect.

Morning light on the Willis palms, San Jacinto, California. These are the native species, Washingtonia filifera. As often happens, fire has burned off most of their skirts.

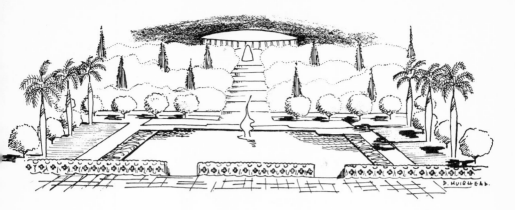

Palms in a formal design.

TOWNS AND GROVES

There has been little thought in this century towards the afforestation of towns. And yet American cities, suffering from the bootless blanket of standardization, have, with only a few notable exceptions, little variety to offer outside their sites, their park systems and their trees. Palms, indeed, can and do give the towns where they are grown an irreplaceable atmosphere of their own.

Where would Miami and Honolulu be without their coconuts? Phoenix, without its *filiferas*, Palm Springs without its *robustas?* La Jolla, Santa Barbara and Los Angeles without their Canary Island dates, Indio without its fruiting dates? Santa Barbara and San Diego can also be said to be characterized by Queen palms, the former city for the better, the latter for the worse. It is hard to understand this in areas where Seaforthias, Howeas, Guadelupes, *Phoenix reclinata, P. rupicola* and *Rophalostylis* can be grown.

This is not to say that palms are the universal answer; they are not. But just as the beauty of the Japanese landscape has been established by good taste in the selection of plant materials as well as a high form of symbolic art, so the future appearance of American cities will depend on the popularity of certain tree species at the nurseries Surely this can be directed.

It is important to note here that palms should be only a part of this scheme. Much of the beauty of San Francisco, for instance, is achieved from the weave through the city of four tree types: the eucalyptus, the Monterey pine, the Monterey cypress, and *Acacia longifolia,* which, together with the hills and the pleasant white urban blocks, form a rich and satisfying textural pattern. Large masses of palms would be out of place, although an occasional *Chamaerops, Howea* or Canary Island date would and does look all right. Farther down the coast at Carmel, the pine, the cypress and the acacia with orange rocks, blue sea, white waves, yellow sand and green, green grass are again enough on their own.

The consistency of the Mediterranean vernacular planting of Santa Barbara is far more attractive than the pseudo-tropical planting of Los Angeles and San Diego, but in all three of these cities palms do look at home. Santa Barbara, once so charming, is now in the hands of the "developers" and is coming apart at the seams. A repetitive use of Canary Island dates, Seaforthias, *Howeas,* Senegal dates, together with good forms of *Eucalyptus citriodora, Acacia longifolia* and Norfolk Island pines would help stabilize the new landscapes in the city. The addition of shrubby species like *Cham-*

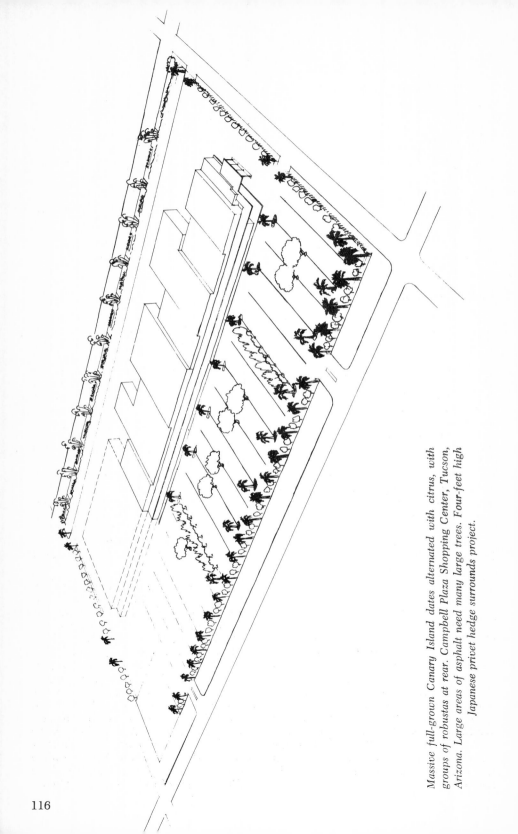

Massive full-grown Canary Island dates alternated with citrus, with groups of robustas at rear. Campbell Plaza Shopping Center, Tucson, Arizona. Large areas of asphalt need many large trees. Four-feet high Japanese privet hedge surrounds project.

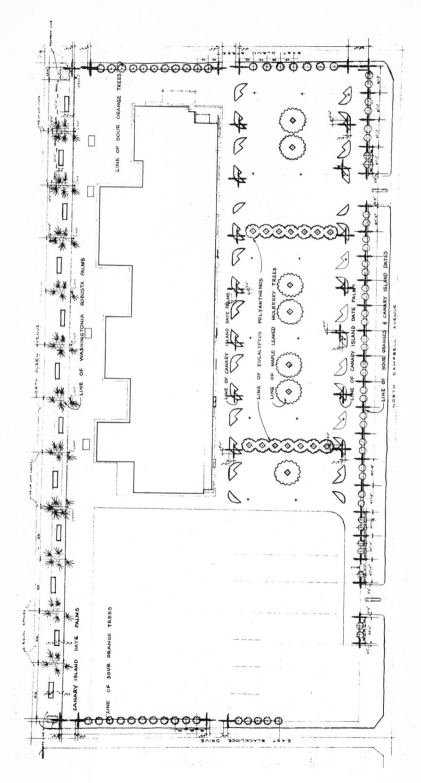

Plan of Campbell Plaza Shopping Center, showing pattern of trees. Area at left is for future expansion.

117

All shopping centers should have the following: Shade for shoppers and their cars. Hedge and strip of lawn to cut off the cars and asphalt from the street. Palms or similar trees for drama and interest.

aerops, Raphidophyllum and *Dracaena draco* with perhaps yuccas, cassias, agaves, aloes and numerous rounded shrubs for balance would continue this desirable character, and cut down the maintenance as well. It would certainly halt the tendency of too many designers (even in Santa Barbara) of retaining live oaks which will die if watered too much, and then adding their full repertoire of shrubs, i.e. the boring old combinations of Pfitzer's juniper, dusty miller and cyperus reed, combined with that ghastly funambulist, our coarse and ugly old friend, *Phormium tenax*, the New Zealand Flax. (Even New Zealanders don't like it.)

Similarly good continuity planting schemes could be worked out for Los Angeles, Palm Springs, San Diego, et al. And palms could play an honest part.

Within the town proper, groves of palms can give a sense of locality to different parts of the city, where areas are becoming as standardized as the individual towns themselves. Indio, is, of course, a good example of grove planting, where old date orchards make excellent unifying elements for any type of large scale landscape planning, especially for sub-divisions, for which they provide a fine sense of shade, shelter and space.

In the tropics graceful palms like coconuts make excellent groves. In fact coconuts and grass by themselves make a most restful and beautiful landscape. Other groves can be created with practically any type of palm in the frost free areas of the world.

In the colder regions Senegal dates, *Chamaerops, Washingtonias, Livistonas, Sabals,* Seaforthias, etc. all make

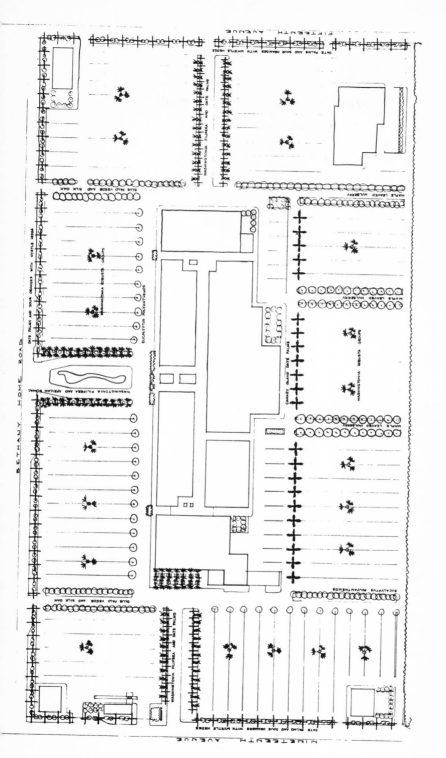

A further step in the right direction. Large tree patterns on the Cristown shopping center, Phoenix, Arizona. Eighty acres of parking broken up by lines of palms, Eucalyptus, mulberries, silk oak, etc., relating the building to the parking and the whole to the tree-lined roads of the city. Blacktop parking areas are the most pressing landscape problems in America today.

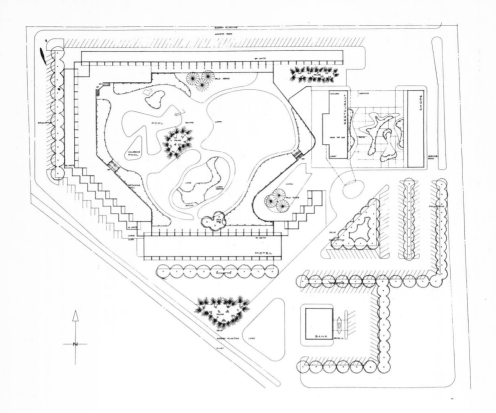

Plan for a 15-acre motel in the desert. Open court, free of cars, gives feeling of oasis. Palms in three groups. Clumps (not shown) *are also planted around project. Parking, building, and landscaping all planned by landscape architect.*

good groves either regularly spaced or in drifts and groups. As a rule palms with stiff upright trunks or large heads, like dates and queen palms, should be spaced well apart, but coconuts or *Washingtonias* can be closely planted, or they can even be placed in clumps in the same hole.

Seaforthias and Howeas can be trained like Coconuts; so can *robustas,* but this is a time-consuming job, although probably a worthwhile one.

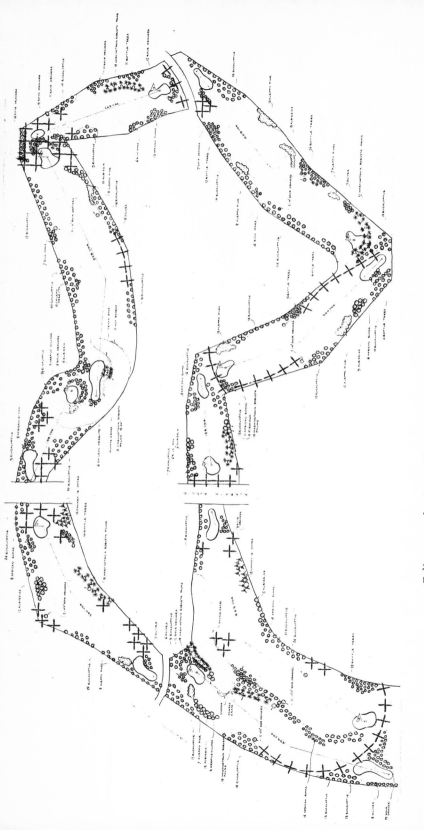

Golf course planting at Sun City, Arizona. Dates (full grown) and robusta used in interesting patterns with many other foliage trees. Fairways are heavily planted as they are surrounded by house in this retirement community. Dates and other palms with large heads should be widely spaced and planted in groups, not clumps.

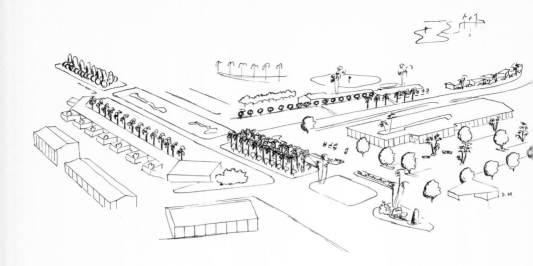

Entrance development for Sun City, Arizona. Motel and apartments on the left; shopping center and active recreation center on the right; model homes are on the extreme right. Bowling green and golf course to the top of the drawing. Lines of dates and citrus, of different lengths, give unity to this diverse building complex. Each 1200-house unit of the city (which, it is anticipated, will eventually have several hundred thousand people) will have a central golf course, thus solving the problem of green open space in a modern subdivision, and also providing for its maintenance. Neighborhood centers such as the above will be scattered at strategic points. Complementary tree patterns for individual streets have been worked out, thus ensuring an eventual beauty far in excess of the houses themselves. Each lot is supplied with three trees. Palms in rows and scattered groups give character to and dominate the skyline of the whole city.

At right, typical tree planting scheme developed for each road at Sun City.

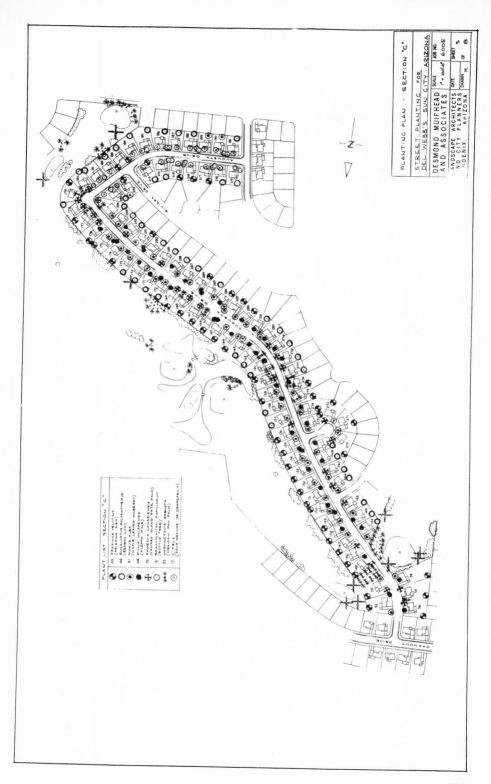

PLANTING PLAN - SECTION 'C'
STREET PLANTING FOR
DEL WEBB'S SUN CITY - ARIZONA
DESMOND MUIRHEAD AND ASSOCIATES
LANDSCAPE ARCHITECTS AND CITY PLANNERS
PHOENIX · ARIZONA

SCALE 1" = 100'   JOB NO. 6005
DATE   SHEET 3
DRAWN   OF 8

N

PLANT LIST - SECTION "C"

●	49	FRAXINUS VELUTINA (ARIZONA ASH)
◉	44	EUCALYPTUS POLYANTHEMUS (SILVER GUM)
●	51	MORUS ALBA (MAPLE LEAVED MULBERRY)
✦	48	PINUS HALEPENSIS (ALEPPO PINE)
○	25	PHOENIX CANARIENSIS (CANARY ISLAND DATE PALM)
✚	9	BRACHYCHITON POPULNEUM (BOTTLE TREE)
✚	21	WASHINGTONIA ROBUSTA (MEXICAN FAN PALM)
⊚	17	CITRUS (SOUR ORANGE OR GRAPEFRUIT)

AUGUSTA DRIVE

RIVIERA

OAKMONT DRIVE

Rich and varying foliage texture available for the designed street. For $10 a lot an area of oak and Albizzia julibrissin. *beauty, regardless of the houses. Palms give character and scale to a combination of silk*

FIELDS AND LINES

If we analyze any man-made or man-altered landscape, we are bound to conclude that the greatest single impact from this landscape seen at ground level comes from a block or a line of trees. Great lines of eucalyptus and Monterey cypress are used as windbreakers in California; cottonwoods, tamarisks and fan palms in Arizona divide up rolling fields of sorghum, corn and cotton, weaving a fabulous foliage texture into the landscape and providing patterns of space in themselves, powerful and unified. The dramatic architecture of eucalyptus windbreaks on the freeway to San Diego just past Anaheim is one memorable example. The blocks of eucalyptus and Monterey cypress outside Melbourne, Australia, is another. Most of these effects are fortuitous, but this does not mean they cannot be planned. Surely, creating such scenes is part of the art of the landscape architect.

Starting from an arbitrary pattern provided by the division of land into field and meadow, a conscious spaceframe can be established with palms, eucalyptus, and other trees, which suggests a huge woven tapestry from a distance and at close quarters is an impressive measure of vertical space. A smaller scale example of this effect is shown on page 111.

In the agricultural landscape, the point and counterpoint of blocks, groves and lines of palms and other trees provided by street, hedgerow, home, and woodland make possibly the greatest and certainly the most stimulating man-made landscape in existence.

Avenue planting has fallen into disrepute of recent years, and yet it is just what the formless landscape of today needs. Lines or avenues of trees leading to farmhouses or public buildings, or bordering drives or streets, are probably as effective when planted

Palms are effectively romantic by all types of water, rivers, lakes or seashores. Most palms grow naturally near water of some kind and like to get some of their roots into water courses. Coconuts do best on shores where they get their roots into underground water, seeping from surrounding hills. Washingtonia filiferas grow near stream beds. The unpruned robusta in the background shows how untidy this palm looks when its skirt is left to the mercy of the wind.

(Below) All palms are fabulous when illuminated. Their form and structure is brought into relief by strong shadows. A circular group of robustas shortly after planting at the Riviera Hotel, Palm Springs. Lighting is more often from ground level.

with palms as with any other type of tree. Palms with straight trunks are necessary for this type of planting. Royal palms, perhaps make the finest avenues in the world. But they will only grow in the warm sub-tropics or in the tropics (see page 84). Princess palms, cohunes, palmyras, talipots, wax palms and many others make good avenues in the tropics. Coconuts make interesting informal avenues.

In the more temperate coastal climates, Guadalupes, *Archontophoenix, Howeas,* and *Livistona australis* are being extensively used, while in the inland valleys and the desert *Washingtonias,* queen palms, Canary Island dates, fruiting dates, Senegal dates, *Sabals, Jubaeas,* Livistonas, Guadalupes and *Edythea brandigeei* are all good. The smaller, thinner palms can be planted 20 feet apart, while the larger, thicker ones like Canary Island dates can have as much as 50 feet between them. Avenues of *robustas* and other tall slender palms lining both sides of narrow walks are particularly effective (see page 110). Other trees in lines, curves, or circles can bring in cross currents of design, and blocks and groves of palms or different trees can be orchestrated with them.

Each successive tree combines impression upon impression until the final result is an inspiring, soaring mass of trunks and waving fronds silhouetted against the sky. This linear planting is very useful with shopping centers where large blocks of asphalt need to be broken up, and where interesting textures help to relieve the vacuumatic sensation of the traditional parking lot. (See pp. 116-119.)

Remember, it takes years of training, plus considerable talent, business acumen and technical ability to put up a building of merit—an end result which must be looked on as a triumph in our society. Yet anyone can plant an avenue of palms and the final impact is greater than a building by Frank Lloyd Wright.

SUBDIVISIONS

The sky is the limit with subdivisions, and something really can be done with them. Trees well selected and planted can eventually provide a street scene which is far more satisfying than the houses alone. The F.H.A., I believe, allows $175 per house for landscaping in the average tract. Anyone concerned with actual costs can see that in most parts of the country only a fraction of this amount is actually spent. And yet, if he were allowed to spend a mere $20 a lot, a sensitive designer could ensure that the subdivision would one day be a place of great beauty.

Let me explain. Some trees form naturally complementary groups like silk oak, *Albizzia* and *robusta* palms. Repeat them down the street and the effect is fabulous. Each home owner can have any combination of three trees. The group impression soars with repetition until the street feels richer than the Palace of Versailles. Of course, the maximum effect the merchant builder can have the whole street laid out. Most landscape architects charge $5 to $10 a lot for this service . . . a small sum to ensure a subdivision worth going back to.

The idea can be expanded indefinitely. You could use *Ficus benjamina, Eucalyptus citriodora* and coconuts in warm subtropical climates. Aleppo or Canary Island pine, palo verde and Chamaerops in the desert. Queen palm, *Thevetia* and giant bamboo nearer the coast. Even olives and *robustas* make a fine street. These different combinations need not be the only trees on the street, but they provide a firm framework into which other trees may fit comfortably without the untidy spot planting too often found in subdivisions.

(Left) A dramatic group of Sabals in perfect equilibrium. These trees are growing wild in Florida.

NIXON SMILEY

A grove of coconuts at Henry Kaiser's Hawaiian Village.

GROUPS AND SINGLE SPECIMENS

The most useful system of planting in the garden is by groups, clumps, or single specimens.

Groups and clumps must be subordinated to the overall design. You cannot go in for every different palm that grows and expect anything but a hideous jumble (page 138). Groups and lines of different species just look untidy like the group at Riverside, California, in the little park at Cypress and 14th.

A collection of palms needs the foil of massed broad-leaved plants and citrus-type trees to tone down the vibrations of the different palms, most of which swear at each other if at all closely planted. *Sabals, Butias,* and other prima donnas should be segregated, and groups should be made of the similar species. Often a very few well-placed palms with lots of broad-leaved trees is most effective (see page 135). Or groups of different species tucked away in patios or other garden corners (see page 138). If you do use groups of different species like *robustas* and Canary Island dates, or Queen palms and *Livistonas,* see that they are of greatly different heights.

Good groups like the palmettos on page 31 can be formed from any naturally upright palm as long as the height variation is maintained. More formal

Senegal dates grow naturally in clumps. They are better with plenty of air around them rather than crowded against buildings like this one in Balboa Park, San Diego.

Date palms make good groups, but they have large heads, so they need wide spacing. They are best planted upright and should be of different heights.

129

(Top) Clumps of even-height palms can have open spaced tops. Palms are always an integral part of the design, not a reason for it.

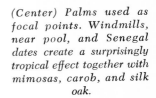

(Center) Palms used as focal points. Windmills, near pool, and Senegal dates create a surprisingly tropical effect together with mimosas, carob, and silk oak.

(Below) A garden in the desert with palms augmented by the rich foliage masses of Dasylirion, artichokes, aloes, bamboos, bananas, citrus, pines, and eucalyptus.

Sabals *and* Chamaerops humilis *used as garden sculpture.*

palms like *robustas* can actually be planted in blocks of different shapes as well.

Single specimens of palms combine better with other trees than with themselves. You can see many island homesteads of luxurious foliage in the simmering desert heat of Arizona, California, and Texas: ash, peppers, pines, and eucalyptus, and here and there a *filifera* or a Canary Island date looking strangely at home in this varied company.

A few suggestions are shown on page 138. After scanning this book, get out a pencil and paper and try some of your own ideas. About the only things you have to worry about are *whether or not palms are appropriate for your area* and whether those palms with trunks show to the ground, or have a foreground of rounded foliage. Spiky plants like yuccas or *Phormium* compete with the form of the palm, if planted too close to them.

A word of warning — no palm will compete with a full-grown, red-blooded, black-hearted telegraph pole, but a group or grove of *filiferas*, dates, or coconuts is the best cure yet devised for one. When will our wealthy power companies be able to afford to put these eyesores underground, as they seem to be able to do without strain in the "poor" countries of western Europe?

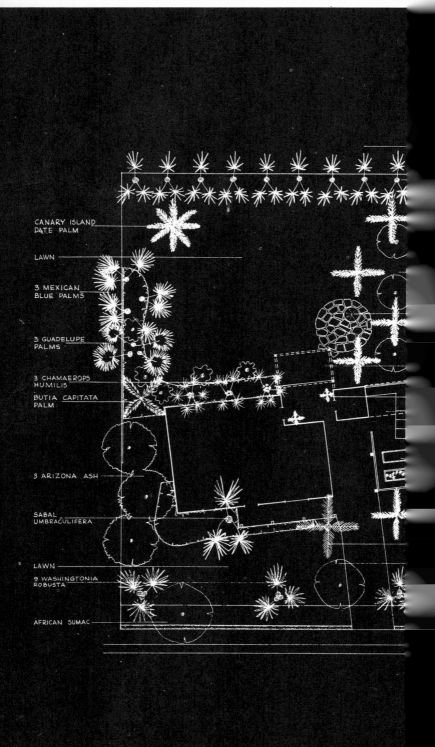

CANARY ISLAND
DATE PALM

LAWN

3 MEXICAN
BLUE PALMS

3 GUADELUPE
PALMS

3 CHAMAEROPS
HUMILIS
BUTIA CAPITATA
PALM

3 ARIZONA ASH

SABAL
UMBRACULIFERA

LAWN
9 WASHINGTONIA
ROBUSTA

AFRICAN SUMAC

A plan of a garden (left) designed for the desert or inland valleys. On the coast, substitute the Guadalupe palm for the filiferas, and Seaforthias for the dates; in the tropics, Royals, or Fiji fans for filiferas and coconuts, latans or Princess palms for the dates. The drawing above shows a view of the rear garden.

A garden with so many palms needs as much round, soft foliage as you can give it. Citrus and Ficus species will help reduce the competition which so many striking forms produce. The groups could be formed of practically any appropriate palm species with small heads. The front garden (above) is again helped by a hedge.

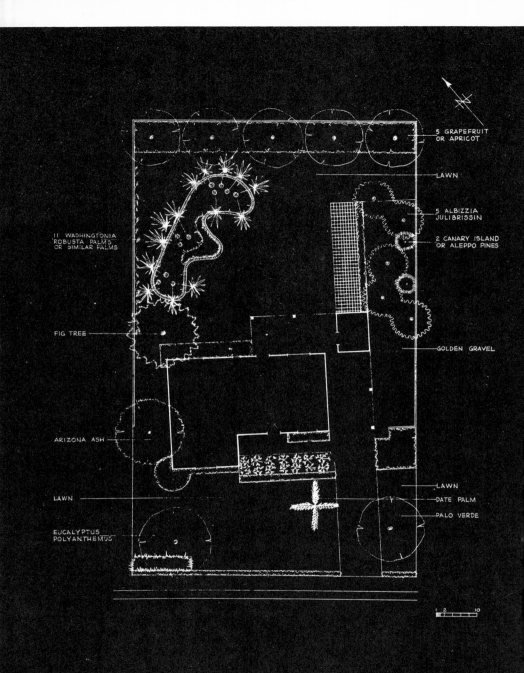

5 GRAPEFRUIT
OR APRICOT

LAWN

5 ALBIZZIA
JULIBRISSIN

11 WASHINGTONIA
ROBUSTA PALMS
OR SIMILAR PALMS

2 CANARY ISLAND
OR ALEPPO PINES

FIG TREE

GOLDEN GRAVEL

ARIZONA ASH

LAWN

LAWN

DATE PALM

PALO VERDE

EUCALYPTUS
POLYANTHEMUS

This garden and the one on the previous page were 2 of 20 typical gardens developed for Sun City, Arizona. The larger elements such as the patio and palm group are floating and can be adapted to any garden of comparable size.

A single group of palms is often all that is needed. This simple garden is composed only of trees, grass and oleander hedge. Trees are (left to right) Chinese elm, Eucalyptus polyanthemos, bottles, palo verde, pine and mulberry.

Palms define the limits of a property. Plants in foreground are Dasylirion, yucca, *giant tree bamboo.*

A NOTE ON THE AMERICAN LANDSCAPE

"There was a time, perhaps 100 years ago, when America was the most beautiful country on earth, now it comes close to being the most ugly." Edward Stone, architect for the U. S. pavilion at the Brussel's World's Fair.

The American landscape is not a limitless resource, and it is being squandered. Once it is gone millions of dollars will be needed to replace it in the shape of much needed city parks. These are slow to take form in the urban sprawl which is rapidly suffocating the hills and dales of this once-lovely countryside.

In Scandinavia beauty is a part of the way of life, and the landscapes of Sweden and Denmark, and, indeed, Holland, and Switzerland are not marred by gas stations, body shops, motels, junk yards, drive-in restaurants, and the other large scale litter which makes hideous the approaches to many American towns. Nor is their countryside defaced with billboards and thoughtlessly placed power lines. In some European countries landscape architects are hired to site the locations of cross-country lines "to subordinate these man-made elements to the landscape and to integrate them with the existing scenery in the most inconspicuous way possible."

Hubert Owens, professor of Landscape Architecture at the University of Georgia, considers America 50 years behind in the laws necessary to build such civic masterpieces as Vallingby and Blackborg in Sweden; and a similar period in attitudes and education necessary to stop the headlong despoilation of the countryside by "developers," contractors, and land sharks with personal profit as their only motive.

Now, there are great works of landscape architecture in this country, such as the national parks and the Tennessee Valley. There are also magnificent throughways, freeways, and parkways. Why can't these isolated examples be spread to produce a landscape which has beauty woven into it as a way of life, rather than looking at it as a luxurious ornament only to be enjoyed on special occasions . . . while in between we must look at power poles, billboards and cyclone fences, instead of the trees and fields and lakes that once were there.

Queen palms and Royals
look their best in lines
or groups of upright specimens.

Study in landscapes at a large scale. Warring factions: litter, clutter, power lines; agriculture, order, and scenery.

This is not the end of the road, but the beginning.

Bibliography

Aleppo Pine, robustas, and Canary Island date.

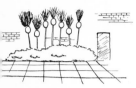

A group of Shaving Brush palms against a protecting wall.

Howeas and tree ferns.

Two Fan palms in a patio.

...ms are prima donnas — don't expect ...m to combine easily. Don't crowd ...m as in this awful group — stage them.

Bailey, Liberty Hyde,
1936. Cyclopedia of American Horticulture. Macmillan Co., New York. 3 vols.
1941. Hortus second. Macmillan Co., New York. 778.

Blatter, Ethelbert,
1926. The Palms of British India and Ceylon. Oxford University Press, London. Out of print. 600 p.

Crowe, Sylvia,
1956. *Tomorrow's Landscape,* Architectural Press, London. 207 p.

Florida State Horticultural Society,
1892 to date. *Proceedings.* Tallahassee, etc.

Hawkes, Alex D.,
The Major Kinds of Palms. Fairchild Tropical Garden, Coconut Grove, Florida.

Hertrich, William,
1951. *Palms and Cycads.* Huntington Library, San Marino, Calif.

Hoyt, Roland Stewart,
1938. Check list for the *Ornamental Plants of Subtropical Regions.* Livingston Press, Los Angeles. 383 p. (Rev. ed. Livingston Press, San Diego, c-1958. 485 p.)

Kuck, Loraine E., and Tongg, Richard C.,
1955. *The Modern Tropical Garden.* Tongg Publishing Co., Honolulu, Hawaii. 250 p.

MacMillan, Hugh Fraser,
1935. *Tropical Planting and Gardening.* 4th ed. MacMillan and Co., Ltd., London. 560 p.
(5th ed. 1943. Reprint 1946.)

McMinn, Howard E. and Maino, Evelyn,
1935. *An Illustrated Manual of Pacific Coast Trees.* University of California Press, Berkeley, Calif. 409 p.

Mowry, Harold,
1955. *Native and Exotic Palms of Florida.* University of Florida, Agricultural Extension Service, Gainesville, Florida. (Extension Service Bulletin 152) 66 p.

Neal, Marie C.,
1948. *In Gardens of Hawaii.* Bernice P. Bishop Museum, Honolulu, Hawaii. (Bernice P. Bishop Museum Special Publication 40) 805 p.

Nehrling, Henry,
My Garden in Florida, Vol. II. American Eagle Press, Estero, Florida.

Rock, Joseph F. C.,
1917. *The Ornamental Trees of Hawaii.* Published under patronage, Honolulu, Hawaii. 210 p.

Smiley, Nixon,
1951. *Subtropical Gardening in Florida.* University of Miami Press, Coral Gables, Florida. 182 p.

various
Proceedings. Florida State Horticultural Society.
Guide to the Atkins Garden. Central Soledad, Cuba.
1956 to date. *Principes.* Palm Society, Miami, Florida.

Mueller, von, Baron Ferdinand,
1891. *Select Extra Tropical Plants.* Melbourne Government Printer. Printed for the government. Now out of print.

DESMOND MUIRHEAD,
the author

is a landscape architect and city planner with offices in Phoenix, Arizona, Honolulu, Hawaii, and Vancouver B.C. He was educated at Cambridge University, England, the University of British Columbia and the University of Oregon.

Mr. Muirhead is widely recognized as an authority on palms and is the leading proponent of their intelligent use in the landscape. He is also renowned as a designer of both cities and landscapes, and has thus had ample opportunity of putting his principles into practice.

Some of his better-known landscape and site-planning projects (with and without palms) include the world-famous Jasper Park Lodge in the Canadian Rockies, the Aluminum town of Kitimat B.C., and Del Webb's new retirement community of Sun City, Arizona. He is at present working as the planning coordinator of Henry Kaiser's fabulous new city of Hawaii Kai in the Hawaiian Islands, while his firm is working in six different states and four Canadian Provinces.

The layout and design of the book were by the author.

ABOUT THE BOOK

Did you know that there is a palm which grows outside in Canada? That some palms produce seeds weighing 50 pounds which take up to 10 years to mature? That millions of the world's population get their food, clothing and shelter from different species of palm trees?

Have you ever felt like planting a date or coconut grove? Or an avenue of Royal palms or Washingtonias? Or are you looking for a suitable palm to plant by your patio or entrance walk?

All these questions and thousands of others are answered in this fascinating book by one of America's outstanding city planners and landscape architects. Desmond Muirhead has in fact given us the first comprehensive study of palms and their uses in the landscape in publishing history. In addition, the origin, identification, cultivation, and recognition of these plant wonders is covered in minute detail, while all species important in the landscape design are illustrated either by pictures taken by famous photographers or by the author's own superb line drawings.

Every home gardener in California, Arizona, New Mexico, Texas, the Gulf Coast, Florida and Hawaii will want to own this book, not to mention all landscape architects, architects, contractors and nurserymen who live in the warmer sections of our country and in other warm temperate and tropical countries of the world. People in the North will be surprised to discover that the Windmill Palm may grow outside in their area, and will find all kinds of popular household palms discussed. In addition, when they visit the warmer states and countries on their vacations, they will be able to recognize the many different palms they see about them.

So open up — impress your friends, confound your enemies, and get your introduction to the wonderful world of palms!